SPECTRAL THEORY

University Texts in the Mathematical Sciences
Advisory Editors, Herbert E. Robbins and Edgar R. Lorch

TITLES PUBLISHED

Derman and Klein PROBABILITY AND STATISTICAL INFERENCE FOR ENGINEERS

Berberian INTRODUCTION TO HILBERT SPACE

Rosenblatt RANDOM PROCESSES

Takács INTRODUCTION TO THE THEORY OF QUEUES

Lorch SPECTRAL THEORY

Jenner RUDIMENTS OF ALGEBRAIC GEOMETRY

Sz.-Nagy, Bela INTRODUCTION TO REA FUNCTIONS AND ORTHOGONAL EXPANSIONS

University Texts in the Mathematical Sciences

Spectral Theory

EDGAR RAYMOND LORCH

Professor of Mathematics
Barnard College
Columbia University

New York · Oxford University Press · 1962

SECOND PRINTING, 1966

Library of Congress Catalogue Card Number: 62-9824
Printed in the United States of America

a Maristella

PREFACE

The present book is the translation of an Italian manuscript containing the lectures which the author delivered during 1953–54 while he served as Visiting Professor at the University of Rome under the Fulbright Act. He remembers with pleasure the very cordial reception accorded on the Peninsula to the original limited edition. In the process of translation a slight expansion of the verbal bulk has been introduced into the writing in order to make the proofs a little more soft. Variations on the present material have been presented in many keys and moods for over twenty years at Columbia University.

An appropriate alternative title might well be "Banach Spaces and Algebras." Indeed, in this restricted number of pages will be found all the classic material which the reader will need in order to make forays on more special theories. For example, in the chapters on Banach spaces and linear transformation theory one will find the Hahn-Banach theorem, the inverse boundedness theorem, and the uniform boundedness principle; also the standard material on reflexivity, adjoint transformations, projections, reducibility, and even a formulation of the mean-ergodic theorem. The chapter on Hilbert space presents all the classic facts on linear functionals and orthonormal sets as well as the preliminary theory of self-adjoint transformations (bounded or not) and resolutions of the identity.

Chapter IV is devoted to the Cauchy theory for operators. It contains the central facts of spectral theory: spectrum, resolvent, the fundamental projections, spectral radius, and the operational calculus. This theory is then applied to the problem of determining the structure of an arbitrary self-adjoint transformation in Hilbert space. Finally in Chapter VI, we consider Banach algebras. These are exclusively commutative and have a unit. We find here a discussion of reducibility, normed fields, ideals, residue rings, homomorphisms and maximal ideals, the radical, the structure space, and the representation theory.

Although there are other works which cover the material of this volume, most of these display encyclopedic tendencies which may well be discouraging to the uninitiated or to the peripheral reader. The present book is presented frankly with the hope of attracting students who at the outset have not committed themselves to dedicating their major energies to the various complex proliferations of this material. On the other hand, they will find, should they subsequently wish to do so, that they are in a position to turn effectively and rapidly in any current direction of research. To borrow a phrase from the workshop—this is a *kernel* and not a *hull* presentation. A partial list of other works in the field will be found at the end of the book. Those interested in bibliographies may consult these titles.

Let us give some idea of the background material needed to approach these pages. It is assumed that the reader has had a small amount of contact with set theory, metric spaces, abstract algebra, and real and complex variable theory. The book should definitely be *abordable* by a mathematics major in a good college and should be usable as a text by any graduate student at the end of the first year. However, a conscious effort has been made so to write it that it will be useful to physicists and engineers who become caught in problems of spectral theory via the net of differential equations. Thus while the material demands past experience in a variety of fields, we proceed on the assumption that more has been forgotten than remembered. A thesis of ours in writing is that the theory of linear operators will be in the future the central trunk around which the fundamental graduate course in analysis will be built. Thus it is of the utmost importance that its principal features be given as accessible a presentation as possible. This calls for an approach which is generous in its demands and complete in its details.

A short note on style. Frequent use is made of quotation marks properly to attract the reader's attention to a linguistic situation in which precision is being sacrificed to brevity. Thus we "attach" a topology to $\mathcal{S}$ or we "consider" the complex space **B** to be real. However, we shall not go as far as to ask the reader to envisage an "incomplete" Banach space. On occasion, we put into parenthesis (with the genuine purpose of being helpful) a short phrase to focus the mind on a difficulty.

There is no formal presentation of exercises. These are to be found in various parts of the text. They occur also at the ends of some of the chapters mixed with a relaxed and informal discussion of examples.

Our warmest thanks go to Professor Enrico Bompiani who invited us to lecture in Italy and first proposed the preparation, in book form, of the lectures which were given at the Istituto di Matematica in Rome and at the Villa Monastero in Varenna on the Lago di Como. We acknowledge a debt of friendship to the late Luigi Fantappié whose interest in "analytic functionals" provided an interesting counterpoint to the present material. We are grateful to

Professors Sterling Berberian and Hugh Gordon and to Mr. Paul Meyer who assumed the onerous task of reading the text with great care and whose many suggestions and corrections improved the manuscript. We also thank Mr. Barnett Glickfeld who compiled the index and, finally, we wish to express our warm appreciation of the constant and kind assistance received at all stages of the enterprise from the staff of Oxford University Press.

E. R. L.

Dyke Farm, Douglas Hill, Maine
July 22, 1961.

CONTENTS

I BANACH SPACES

II LINEAR TRANSFORMATIONS

III HILBERT SPACE

SPECTRAL THEORY

I BANACH SPACES

1. On structure

Structure is the key word to the understanding of any branch of mathematics. This fact, which now has become elementary as well as elemental, has been the property of mathematicians for some time. However, it was the modern school of mathematics in France which first formulated the concept and claimed for it the full scope which it plays in our science.[1] Inherent in the notion is that every mathematical system (another expression for "mathematical subject") has a given structure, which differentiates it sharply from other systems neighboring or distant, and by which it is known and recognized. Fortunately, knowledge of the structure of a mathematical system can be obtained very rapidly in that it is possible for the mathematician to set down the few motivating principles, "la charpente préliminaire," on which the entire edifice is raised. Once these basic assumptions or principles have been set down, the course has been fixed and it merely remains for the scientist to elaborate the consequences.

Without attempting to enter into a highly focused definition of structure, let us suggest that the structure of a system is delineated when the axioms of the system have been set down. Thus the theory of groups, of rings, of topological spaces, is completely forecast when the axioms of the system are formally

[1] See the works of N. Bourbaki, in particular, *La théorie des ensembles*, Actualités Sci. Ind., Paris.

written down, the theory itself then consisting of the body of logical consequences of that system of axioms. This is the essence of the axiomatic method. It is interesting to note that essentially all branches of mathematics have been axiomatized (or could be without too much fatigue) and that this has been done principally in the last two generations, thus, very recently.

Discussion of mathematical systems via the notion of structure, that is, discussing them via the axiomatic approach, places natural implications on the entire course of development. Automatically, the schism between the deductive and inductive approach to learning is resolved in favor of the former. An observation may be made at this point. Each of the two approaches to the learning of mathematical disciplines is correct at certain stages of development. In particular, the inductive approach seems the only possible one to use on the young pupil. At the other end of the scale of age and experience, the trained scientist (engineer, mathematician, or physicist) can assimilate much more rapidly by learning via the deductive method. This is the situation for us. The implications are that we shall *begin* by setting down our axioms and only subsequently (some pages or sections later) shall we give examples. Frequently, the examples will be in the form of a rapid delineation, the elaboration of which is left to the reader "as an exercise." Although all traces of sadism cannot be eliminated from a manuscript, it is incorrect and unfair to impute to most authors malevolent intentions in this respect. Usually, limitations of space on the page and energy in the writer are the raison d'être of the exercise that the reader solves only after five months.

2. The axioms

The structure which we wish to define is that of a Banach space. Roughly speaking, a Banach space is a real or complex vector space which has a norm and which enjoys the topological property of completeness with respect to that norm. Thus we begin by considering the axioms of a vector space. However, before making statements which are precise let us make some that are suggestive. A vector space **B** is a collection of objects which will be denoted by $f,g,h, \cdots$ and for which two operations are defined: addition which is written $f + g$ and scalar multiplication which is written αf or $\alpha \cdot f$. The fact that the only scalars which interest us will be real or complex reveals that the present work is in the field of analysis. With respect to addition and scalar multiplication, the vectors satisfy the "usual algebraic laws," a phrase which in the present instance has far more positive than negative value and deserves to be used. In fact, the reader without experience in axiomatics is urged to let his previously developed algebraic reflexes guide him without fear.

More precisely: Consider a set **B** having elements $f, g, h, \cdots$. Let **B** be a commutative group written additively. This implies that if $f \in \mathbf{B}, g \in \mathbf{B}, h \in \mathbf{B}$, then $f + g \in \mathbf{B}$;[2] that $f + g = g + f$; that $f + (g + h) = (f + g) + h$; that there exists a unique element $0 \in \mathbf{B}$ such that $f + 0 = f$; that to each f in **B** there exists a unique element $-f$ such that $f + (-f) = 0$. We note that $f + (-g)$ is usually written $f - g$.

Furthermore, let $\mathfrak{F}$ denote the field of real numbers or the field of complex numbers whose members are $\alpha, \beta, \gamma, \cdots$. Let **B** admit $\mathfrak{F}$ as a set of operators: That is, there is given a mapping $(\alpha, f) \to \alpha \cdot f$ with $\alpha f \in \mathbf{B}$; for this mapping we have:

$$(1) \qquad \begin{aligned} \alpha(f + g) &= \alpha f + \alpha g; \\ (\alpha + \beta)f &= \alpha f + \beta f; \\ (\alpha\beta)f &= \alpha(\beta f); \\ 1 \cdot f &= f. \end{aligned}$$

[2] We shall use freely the notations of elementary set theory. Thus $f \in B$ means "the element f belongs to the set B." Similarly, $A \cup B$, $A \cap B$, $A = B$ mean respectively "the set theoretic union of A and B," "the set theoretic intersection of A and B," "the sets A and B have the same elements." Sets are frequently denoted by braces; thus $\{a, b\}$, $\{f_n\}$ are two sets whose elements are respectively a and b and f_n, $n = 1,2, \cdots$.

DEFINITION 2-1: *The object* **B** *satisfying the above relations is called a vector space over* $\mathfrak{F}$. *If* $\mathfrak{F}$ *is the field of real numbers,* **B** *is called a real vector space. If* $\mathfrak{F}$ *is the field of complex numbers,* **B** *is called a complex vector space.*

Examples abound. We shall give at this point a few elementary ones. Let us remind ourselves of the precise procedure in giving an example correctly. One must specify the two functions: $(f, g) \to f + g$ and $(\alpha, f) \to \alpha f$. Having done that, it remains to check that **B** with these operations satisfies the axioms. In case the operations of addition and scalar multiplication should not be specified, it will be understood that they are the "usual ones" for the set **B** in question.

The real field or the complex field with the usual operations is a real or a complex vector space. Note that each field acts upon itself with respect to scalar multiplication. The complex field may be considered also a real vector space. The set of polynomials in one variable with coefficients in $\mathfrak{F}$ is a vector space. Here, once more, the operations of addition and scalar multiplication are obvious. The set of real or complex functions defined on some fixed set $\mathcal{E}$ is a vector space—the operations being the usual ones. Note that the set **B** consisting of one element only $\mathbf{B} = \{0\}$ is a vector space (a very important one) if **B** is the group with one element and if one defines $\alpha \cdot 0 = 0$ for all $\alpha \in \mathfrak{F}$.

Finally, the set of all n-tuples $x = (x_1, \cdots, x_n)$, $x_i \in \mathfrak{F}$, $i = 1, \cdots, n$ is a vector space, $\mathbf{l}_n$, (over $\mathfrak{F}$, *bien entendu*) providing one defines the operations by

$$(x_1, \cdots, x_n) + (y_1, \cdots, y_n) = (x_1 + y_1, \cdots, x_n + y_n)$$

and

$$\alpha(x_1, \cdots, x_n) = (\alpha x_1, \cdots, \alpha x_n).$$

In this example $0 = (0, \cdots, 0)$ and $-(x_1, \cdots, x_n) = (-x_1, \cdots, -x_n)$. It should be noted that this example is a special case of one above; we are considering the set of scalar-valued functions on a set $\mathcal{E}$ having n points. The case $n = 2$ or

3 is interesting for historical reasons. If one represents the vector (x_1, x_2) by an arrow extending from the origin in the Cartesian plane to the point whose co-ordinates are x_1 and x_2, one finds that vector addition is precisely addition in accordance to the parallelogram law as required by so many phenomena in physics.

We now introduce the notion of norm. Roughly speaking, the notion of norm allows us to introduce the notion of length and many of its principal attributes into a vector space. The reader is warned that there are many lengths possible besides the Euclidean one. For a vector $f \in \mathbf{B}$, the length or *norm* of f is denoted by $\|f\|$. It is a real number.

More precisely:

DEFINITION 2-2: *A vector space* **B** *is said to be normed if there is given a real-valued function defined over* **B**: $f \to \|f\|$ *having the following properties:*

(2a) $\|f\| \geq 0$; $\|f\| = 0$ if and only if $f = 0$;

(2b) $\|\alpha f\| = |\alpha| \cdot \|f\|$;

(2c) $\|f + g\| \leq \|f\| + \|g\|$.

The third inequality is called the *triangle inequality* since that classical inequality in Euclidean geometry is a special case of it. The reader is advised that he should supply appropriate quantifiers in reading the above statements. For example, $\|f\| \geq 0$ is to be read "for all $f \in \mathbf{B}$, $\|f\| \geq 0$." It should be noted that a vector space may become a normed space in more ways than one. If **B** is a vector space in which a norm function $\|\cdot\|$ has been introduced, the normed space is the pair $(\mathbf{B}, \|\cdot\|)$. However, for brevity we shall speak of **B** itself being a normed vector space. (We had the same difficulty before but did not mention it: vector spaces should have been denoted by the complex $(\mathbf{B}, \mathfrak{F}, \text{“}+\text{,” “}\cdot\text{”})$ where **B** is the set, $\mathfrak{F}$ is the field of scalars, and the other symbols represent the functions defining addition and multiplication; in other words the symbols following **B** define the structure. For the sake of brevity the set **B** with its structure is denoted by **B**. This leads to embarassing situations later on which will be met according to the constitution of the individual with or without a mathematical blush. For example, one may say: "Take the normed space **B** and introduce into it a new norm." Or "Consider the normed space **B** just as a vector space, hence devoid of a norm.")

The postulating of a norm allows one to introduce topological notions into the vector space **B**. It is important (and a source of satisfaction, too) that the topology in question is that of a metric space, that is, the easiest type with which to deal. We remind the reader that a set $\mathcal{E}$ has the structure of a metric space if there is defined for every pair (x, y) of points in $\mathcal{E}$ a real-valued function $d(x, y)$—read: distance from x to y—satisfying the following axioms:

(3a) $d(x, y) \geq 0$; $d(x, y) = 0$ if and only if $x = y$;

(3b) $d(x, y) = d(y, x)$;

(3c) $d(x, z) \leq d(x, y) + d(y, z)$.

If now **B** is a normed vector space, then the real-valued function $d(f, g) = \|f - g\|$ has all the properties of a distance function. In particular, the three conditions in (2) establish the corresponding three conditions in (3). Having established this fact, we are in a position to introduce into our discussion the entire vocabulary of metric spaces: sphere, neighborhood, open, closed, connected, compact, separable, complete, etc.

We illustrate by considering the notion of completeness. A sequence $\{x_n\}$ in a metric space $\mathcal{E}$ is said to be a Cauchy sequence if and only if $d(x_n, x_m) \to 0$ as $n \to \infty$. Given such a sequence, there may or may not exist an element $x \in \mathcal{E}$ such that

$$d(x, x_n) \to 0$$

as $n \to \infty$; that is, such that $x_n \to x$. In case each Cauchy sequence in the space does converge to an element in the space, the space is called *complete*.

We are ready now to add the last element of structure in our definition of a Banach space.

DEFINITION 2-3: *A normed vector space* **B** *is called a Banach space if and only if the space* **B** *is complete in the metric defined by the norm.*[3]

Let us consider some examples. Most important (almost the cardinal fact of all analysis) is the fact that the real and complex fields are Banach spaces providing the norm $\|\cdot\|$ is taken to be the absolute value $|\cdot|$ of the scalar in question. Next, consider the set of real functions, which are defined and continuous on the closed interval [0, 1]. This set will be denoted by $\mathbf{C}_{[0,1]}$. If f denotes such a function (some readers may feel happier with the more dangerous notation $f(x)$!), let

$$\|f\| = \sup_{0\leq x\leq 1} |f(x)|. \tag{4}$$

It is not difficult to see, using well-known properties of continuous functions, that the function $f \to \|f\|$ is a norm function. Using another property of continuous functions, one may see that $\mathbf{C}_{[0,1]}$ is complete in this norm and hence is a Banach space. More generally, let $\mathfrak{M}$ be a topological space and let $\mathbf{C}_{\mathfrak{M}}$ denote the totality of bounded continuous real-valued functions defined over $\mathfrak{M}$. If the vector operations are defined as usual and the norm is that given by

$$\|f\| = \sup_{x\in\mathfrak{M}} |f(x)|, \tag{5}$$

we have once more a Banach space. The spaces $\mathbf{C}_{\mathfrak{M}}$ are very important and have received much attention.

Note that the set of real polynomials in one variable does not constitute a Banach space if the norm is chosen as in (4) because completeness is not at hand. This is because there are continuous functions which are not polynomials.

[3] These spaces became famous immediately after the publication of Banach's book in 1932. Banach himself refers to them as "espaces du type B."

We shall now consider the arithmetic n-space, $\mathbf{l}_n$, introduced earlier and "make it into a Banach space." This means that we shall introduce a norm function in which the given space is complete. Whereas before, we were discussing situations in which there was a "usual" norm, we are now confronted with a substantial choice of possible norms. Let us list a few of these and suggest to the reader that any immediate desire to order them according to importance probably has an emotional rather than a logical background. For $x = (x_1, \cdots, x_n)$, let

$$\|x\| = \sum_{i=1}^{n} |x_i|; \tag{6a}$$

$$\|x\| = \sup_{1 \leq i \leq n} |x_i|; \tag{6b}$$

$$\|x\| = \left(\sum_{i=1}^{n} |x_i|^2\right)^{1/2}; \tag{6c}$$

$$\|x\| = \left(\sum_{i=1}^{n} |x_i|^p\right)^{1/p}, \ 1 < p < \infty. \tag{6d}$$

In each case one obtains a Banach space. These various structures are denoted by $\mathbf{l}_n^1$, $\mathbf{l}_n^\infty$, $\mathbf{l}_n^2$, and $\mathbf{l}_n^p$ respectively. The reader should establish the Banach space character, being advised in advance that while cases (6a) and (6b) are easy to handle, the remaining two require a toolbox of inequalities (Cauchy, Euclid, Hölder, Minkowski).

We shall consider more sophisticated examples later in the chapter.

3. Linear functionals

If **B** is a Banach space (real or complex), a functional on **B** is a mapping, that is, a function, from **B** to the scalars (real or complex). For example, the norm function $f \to \|f\|$ is a functional. Functionals will be denoted by F, G, H, $\cdots$. The value of F for the vector $f \in \mathbf{B}$ will be denoted by Ff or $F(f)$. The functional F is said to be linear if

$$F(f + g) = Ff + Fg; \tag{7a}$$
$$F(\alpha f) = \alpha(Ff), \tag{7b}$$

the equations being valid for all choices of the indicated vectors and scalars. The functional F will be said to be bounded in case there exists a real constant $\mathrm{k} \geq 0$ such that for all $f \in \mathbf{B}$

$$|Ff| \leq \mathrm{k}\|f\|. \tag{8}$$

For bounded functionals there is always a least value of k satisfying (8) and that value is (with good reason as we shall see) denoted by $\|F\|$ and is called the *bound* or the *norm* of F. We shall be interested almost exclusively in bounded linear functionals. When the word "functional" appears in a discussion the reader may presume that the functional is of this type.

We have seen that a normed space has a metric and hence we may raise questions concerning functionals which are continuous with respect to this metric. We shall show now that

A linear functional F is bounded if and only if it is continuous.

Proof: Let F be bounded. Then we have for any two vectors f and g

$$|Ff - Fg| = |F(f - g)| \leq \|F\| \cdot \|f - g\|.$$

The above relation states that if $\|f - g\|$ is "small," then $|Ff - Fg|$ is also "small." In other words F is continuous.

Suppose now that F is not bounded. We shall see that F is not continuous. Since F is not bounded there exists elements $f \in \mathbf{B}$ for which $|Ff|/\|f\|$ is arbitrarily large. Using (7b) we may assume that $\|f\| = 1$. Thus we may choose a sequence $\{f_n\}$, $\|f_n\| = 1$, such that $|Ff_n| \geq n$. This means that $|Fg_n| \geq 1$ where $g_n = f_n/n$. Now $\{g_n\}$ converges to *0* since $\|g_n\| = 1/n$. If F is continuous at O, Fg_n converges to $FO = 0$. This is impossible since $|Fg_n| \geq 1$. Thus F is not continuous. Note that we have used the fact that $FO = 0$. This is proved as follows: If f is arbitrary, then $FO = F(0 \cdot f) = 0 \cdot Ff = 0$.

We see now that the bounded linear functionals are a topologically distinguished collection.

A particularly important bounded linear functional is defined by $Of = 0$ for all f. Note that $\|O\| = 0$.

We propose now to introduce operations in the set of all bounded linear functionals in such a way that this set becomes a Banach space. Before doing this let us pause to see what the task entails: We must define the addition and scalar multiplication of functionals. We must define the norm (already done). We must show that with respect to these operations, all our axioms, largely in the form of equalities or inequalities, are satisfied. To complete the task requires, in this case, some ten to fifteen operations. These operations must be performed whether the time required for them be one day or one microsecond. The new initiate is warned to interpret correctly the aloof and seemingly disinterested attitude of the expert who seems to get good results by waving his hand alla Prospero. And now down to the task.

DEFINITION 3-1: *If F and G are functionals, then $F + G$ represents the functional whose value at f is*

$$(F + G)f = Ff + Gf. \tag{9}$$

Similarly, αF represents the functional whose value at f is

$$(\alpha F)f = \alpha(Ff). \tag{10}$$

We make an important observation. In many cases, it is wiser to replace (10) by

$$(\alpha F)f = \bar{\alpha}(Ff), \tag{11}$$

where $\bar{\alpha}$ is the complex conjugate of α. We shall return to this later in connection with the work on Hilbert space but shall not further emphasize it here.

Finally, we remind the reader of the meaning of equality: $F = G$. Since F and G are mappings (or functions), we have

$$\text{(12)} \qquad F = G \textit{ if and only if } Ff = Gf \textit{ for all } f \in \mathbf{B}.$$

Having defined "+," " · ," and $\|\cdot\|$ for linear functionals we state formally our proposition.

THEOREM 3-1: *With respect to the operations of addition, scalar multiplication, and taking of the norm, the totality of bounded linear functionals on a Banach space* **B** *constitutes a Banach space which will be denoted by* **B***.

Partial proof: Consider closure under addition: To show that if F and G are bounded linear functionals, so is $F + G$. We have

$$\text{(13)} \qquad \begin{aligned} (F + G)(f + g) &= F(f + g) + G(f + g) \\ &= (Ff + Fg) + (Gf + Gg) \\ &= (Ff + Gf) + (Fg + Gg) \\ &= (F + G)f + (F + G)g, \end{aligned}$$

the first and last equalities being valid by virtue of the definition (9), the second by virtue of the linearity of F and G, the third by virtue of properties of scalars. Similarly one may prove that $(F + G)(\alpha f) = \alpha[(F + G)f]$. Next, we have

$$\text{(14)} \qquad \begin{aligned} |(F + G)f| &= |Ff + Gf| \leq |Ff| + |Gf| \\ &\leq \|F\|\,\|f\| + \|G\|\,\|f\| = (\|F\| + \|G\|)\|f\|. \end{aligned}$$

This shows that $F + G$ is bounded and at the same time establishes the triangle inequality $\|F + G\| \leq \|F\| + \|G\|$.

The various group properties of **B*** are easily established, keeping in mind (12).

Assuming everything else has been taken care of, let us look at the question of completeness. Let $\{F_n\}$ be a Cauchy sequence in $\mathbf{B}^*: \|F_n - F_m\| \to 0$. Let f be a fixed element in **B**. Then since

$$|F_nf - F_mf| = |(F_n - F_m)f| \leq \|F_n - F_m\| \, \|f\|,$$

$\{F_nf\}$ is a Cauchy sequence of scalars. Since the field of scalars is complete, the limit of $\{F_nf\}$ exists and will be denoted by Ff: $F_nf \to Ff$. This defines a function F from **B** to the field of scalars. It remains to show that F is bounded and linear and that $F_n \to F$, meaning that $\|F - F_n\| \to 0$. Linearity is easy to handle since F_n is linear. For boundedness, important use is made of the fact that for any Cauchy sequence $\{F_n\}$, the sequence of scalars $\{\|F_n\|\}$ is bounded: $\|F_n\| \leq$ k. The remaining steps are now straightforward. Thus the theorem has been proved.

The space $\mathbf{B}^*$ is called the *adjoint* of **B** (also the *dual* or the *conjugate* of **B**).

Given this result, we may now discuss an important problem of analysis: *Given a specific Banach space,* **B**, *to construct explicitly the space of all bounded linear functionals on* **B**. The problem may be clarified somewhat by the following rapid considerations. The set of all Banach spaces contains with any given space **B**, the space $\mathbf{B}^*$ and also the spaces $\mathbf{B}^{**} = (\mathbf{B}^*)^*$, $\mathbf{B}^{***}$, etc. The problem calls for the successful pairing $(\mathbf{B}, \mathbf{B}^*)$ of couples of elements in this set. Examples of results along this line are: The space adjoint to $\mathbf{l}_n^p$, $1 < p < \infty$, is $\mathbf{l}_n^q$ where q is defined by $1/p + 1/q = 1$. Another example (very famous) is the following: If **B** is the space $\mathbf{C}_{[0,1]}$ of all continuous functions on $[0, 1]$, then $\mathbf{B}^*$ is essentially the set of all functions of bounded variation α where the functional F_α generated by α is defined by the Riemann-Stieltjes integral

$$F_\alpha f = \int_0^1 f(t) \, d\alpha(t). \tag{15}$$

Problems of this type have received an enormous amount of

attention during the first part of this century. We shall mention a few of them later in the chapter.

4. The canonical map

We shall show now that there is a "natural" manner in which the space **B** may be considered to be a subspace of $\mathbf{B}^{**}$. To this effect, let f be a fixed element in **B**. Consider the functional f^{**} defined over $\mathbf{B}^{*}$ by means of

$$f^{**}F = Ff. \tag{16}$$

It is easy to see that f^{**} is linear and bounded and hence belongs to $\mathbf{B}^{**}$. Since $|f^{**}F| = |Ff| \leq \|f\|\,\|F\|$, we have that $\|f^{**}\| \leq \|f\|$. We see therefore that the mapping $\Phi: f \to f^{**}$ is well defined from **B** into $\mathbf{B}^{**}$. This mapping is a homomorphism, that is, it has the properties:

$$\begin{gathered} f + g \to f^{**} + g^{**}; \\ \alpha f \to \alpha f^{**}. \end{gathered} \tag{17}$$

We may also write: $(f + g)^{**} = f^{**} + g^{**}$ and $(\alpha f)^{**} = \alpha f^{**}$. We shall be able to prove later that $\|f^{**}\| = \|f\|$ and hence the mapping is an isomorphism. These facts imply that under this mapping, which will be called the *canonical mapping* or the *natural mapping* of **B** into $\mathbf{B}^{**}$, the space **B** may be considered to be a part of $\mathbf{B}^{**}$. In particular, we introduce

DEFINITION 4-1: *If the image of* **B** *under the above canonical isomorphism is all of* $\mathbf{B}^{**}$, *the space* **B** *is called reflexive.*[4]

Reflexive spaces play an important role in analysis. All finite-dimensional spaces are reflexive. (Sketch of a proof: If **B** is

[4] The term reflexive was introduced by the author in a study of these spaces in 1939. The reflexive property had been individualized by Hahn in 1927 who used the adjective "regular." It is quite clear from the mere definition that reflexive spaces possess important properties not shared by Banach spaces in general.

n-dimensional, then $\mathbf{B}^*$ is also n-dimensional. Hence $\mathbf{B}^{**}$ is also n-dimensional. Since an isomorphism preserves dimensionality the canonical map of $\mathbf{B}$ into $\mathbf{B}^{**}$ is an onto mapping and $\mathbf{B}$ is reflexive.) The spaces $\mathbf{L}^p$, $1 < p < \infty$, to be introduced later, are reflexive. The space $\mathbf{C}_{[0,1]}$ is not reflexive.

5. Subspaces and orthogonality

We start with

DEFINITION 5-1: *If* $\mathbf{M}$ *is a subset of a Banach space* $\mathbf{B}$ *which contains* $f + g$ *and* αf *whenever it contains* f *and* g, *then* $\mathbf{M}$ *is called a linear manifold. If, in addition,* $\mathbf{M}$ *is a closed subset of* $\mathbf{B}$, *it is called a closed linear manifold.*

Closed linear manifolds are frequently referred to as *subspaces;* they are also called at times *manifolds.* Let us consider a few elementary theorems.

THEOREM 5-1: *If* $\mathbf{M}$ *is any subset of* $\mathbf{B}$, *the smallest linear manifold containing* $\mathbf{M}$ *is the set of all vectors of the form* $\alpha_1 f_1 + \cdots + \alpha_n f_n$ *where* n *is an arbitrary natural number,* $f_1, \cdots, f_n$ *are arbitrary in* $\mathbf{M}$ *and* $\alpha_1, \cdots, \alpha_n$ *are arbitrary scalars.*

The proof is trivial.

THEOREM 5-2: *If* $\mathbf{M}$ *is any linear manifold in* $\mathbf{B}$, *the closure in the norm topology of* $\mathbf{M}$ *is a closed linear manifold.*

The proof is based on the fact: If $f_n \to f$ and $g_n \to g$, then $f_n + g_n \to f + g$ and $\alpha f_n \to \alpha f$.

THEOREM 5-3: *If* $\mathbf{M}$ *is a closed linear manifold and* g *is a vector not in* $\mathbf{M}$, *then the totality of vectors of the form* $f + \alpha g$, $f \in \mathbf{M}$, α *arbitrary, is a closed linear manifold.*

Proof: It is clear that the totality is a linear manifold $\mathbf{N}$. Note incidentally that the representation of a vector in the manifold is unique. That is, if $f + \alpha g = f' + \alpha' g$, then $(\alpha' - \alpha)g = f - f'$. If $\alpha' - \alpha \neq 0$, then $g = (\alpha' - \alpha)^{-1}(f - f')$ which is a vector in M. Thus $\alpha = \alpha'$ and $f = f'$.

Suppose now that $\{f_n + \alpha_n g\}$ is a Cauchy sequence in **N**. If the sequence $\{\alpha_n\}$ contains a bounded subsequence, it contains a convergent subsequence. In this case, we may and shall suppose that $\{\alpha_n\}$ itself is this convergent subsequence. If $\alpha_n \rightarrow \alpha$ then we see quickly that $\{f_n\}$ is a Cauchy sequence. Since M is closed, suppose $f_n \rightarrow f \in$ M. Then $f_n + \alpha_n g \rightarrow f + \alpha g$. This proves closure for this case.

Next suppose $\{\alpha_n\}$ contains no bounded subsequence. This means that $|\alpha_n| \rightarrow \infty$. Thus the sequence $\{g + f_n/\alpha_n\}$ converges to zero (since for each n, $\|f_n + \alpha_n g\| < \mathrm{k}$ for some k). That is, $-f_n/\alpha_n \rightarrow g$. Since M is closed, $g \in$ M. This contradiction shows that the present case does not arise.

THEOREM 5-4: *If* M *is a linear manifold and F is a functional which is linear and bounded on* M, *then there exists a unique functional $\bar{F}$ which is defined on the closure* $\bar{\mathrm{M}}$ *of* M, *which is linear and bounded on* $\bar{\mathrm{M}}$ *and which agrees with F on* M.

Elements of a proof: Let $f \in \bar{\mathrm{M}}$ and let $f_n \rightarrow f$ with $f_n \in$ M. Since F is bounded, $|Ff| \leq \mathrm{k}\,\|f\|$. Thus we have $|Ff_n - Ff_m| = |F(f_n - f_m)| \leq \mathrm{k}\|f_n - f_m\|$. Hence $\{Ff_n\}$ is a Cauchy sequence. Define: $\bar{F}f = \lim Ff_n$. It should be noted that $\lim Ff_n$ is independent of the particular sequence $\{f_n\}$ which converges to f. It may then be shown that $\bar{F}$ has the properties of the theorem.

THEOREM 5-5: *Let* M *be a closed linear manifold and let g in* B *not belong to* M. *On the closed linear manifold of elements of the form $f + \alpha g$, $f \in$* M, *define a functional F by $F(f + \alpha g) = \alpha$. Then F is bounded and linear on this manifold.*

Note first that since the representation of an element in the form $f + \alpha g$ is unique, the functional F is well defined. It is obviously linear. Let us suppose for a moment that it is not bounded. Then there exists a sequence $\{f_n + \alpha_n g\}$ for which

$\|f_n + \alpha_n g\| = 1$ and $|\alpha_n| = |F(f_n + \alpha_n g)| \to \infty$. This implies that $\|f_n/\alpha_n + g\| \to 0$, thus that $-f_n/\alpha_n \to g$. Thus g is a limit of elements in **M** and since **M** is closed, $g \in$ **M**. This contradiction shows that our assumption is incorrect. F is bounded.

DEFINITION 5-2: *If* **M** *is a closed linear manifold in* **B** *then* $\mathbf{M}^\perp$ *represents the set of all bounded linear functionals F in* $\mathbf{B}^*$ *such that* $Ff = 0$ *for each* $f \in$ **M**.

The elements in $\mathbf{M}^\perp$ are said to be orthogonal to those in **M** and $\mathbf{M}^\perp$ is called the orthogonal complement of **M**. We shall frequently write $F \perp \mathbf{M}$ to indicate that $F \in \mathbf{M}^\perp$. According to the definition, the manifold $\mathbf{M}^{\perp\perp}$ is in the space $\mathbf{B}^{**}$. If **B** is reflexive, then we may consider that $\mathbf{M}^{\perp\perp}$ is in **B**. Even in the non-reflexive case the symbol $\mathbf{M}^{\perp\perp}$ may be intended to represent vectors in **B** exclusively. We shall not have this difficulty and shall not refer to it further except to note that it is clear from this point of view that $\mathbf{M} \subset \mathbf{M}^{\perp\perp}$.

THEOREM 5-6: *The set* $\mathbf{M}^\perp$ *is a closed linear manifold.*

The proof is trivial.

6. The Hahn-Banach theorem

The Hahn-Banach theorem gives the solution of a particular extension problem. In the general extension problem one considers a mathematical object (for example a function) defined on a substructure of a given structure. The problem consists in extending this object to the entire structure without losing certain characteristic properties. For example, let $\mathfrak{M}$ be a subset of a topological space $\mathcal{S}$ and let f be a real continuous function defined on $\mathfrak{M}$. Let it be required to extend f to all of $\mathcal{S}$ in such a way as to be continuous (this is obviously not always possible).

The Hahn-Banach theorem considers only one of several types of extensions. Much literature has been published on related points. Our proof (for the real case) is essentially that given by Hahn.

THEOREM 6-1: *Let* **B** *be a real Banach space and let* **M** *be a linear manifold (not necessarily closed) in* **B**. *Let* F *be a real functional defined over* **M** *which is linear and bounded. Write* $\|F\|_{\mathbf{M}}$ *for the bound of* F. *Then there exists a bounded linear functional* G *defined over* **B** *such that* (1) $Gf = Ff$ *for* $f \in \mathbf{M}$; (2) $\|G\| = \|F\|_{\mathbf{M}}$.

The proof is in two stages. The first stage consists in extending F by the smallest possible step. Let $g \in \mathbf{B}$, $g \notin \mathbf{M}$. Consider the linear manifold **N** consisting of all elements of the form $f + \alpha g$, $f \in \mathbf{M}$, α arbitrary. We write

$$\mathbf{N} = \{f + \alpha g : f \in \mathbf{M},\ \alpha \text{ arbitrary}\}.$$

We have seen that the representation $f + \alpha g$ is unique (see the proof of theorem 5-3). Let f' and f'' represent elements in **M**. Then since

$$\begin{aligned} Ff' - Ff'' = F(f' - f'') &\leq \|F\|_{\mathbf{M}} \|f' - f''\| \\ &\leq \|F\|_{\mathbf{M}} \|(f' + g) - (f'' + g)\| \\ &\leq \|F\|_{\mathbf{M}} \|f' + g\| + \|F\|_{\mathbf{M}} \|f'' + g\|, \end{aligned}$$

we have

$$(18) \qquad -\|F\|_{\mathbf{M}} \|f'' + g\| - Ff'' \leq \|F\|_{\mathbf{M}} \|f' + g\| - Ff'.$$

Letting f' and f'' vary independently over **M**, we see that the supremum S of the quantity on the left of (18) is inferior to ($\leq$) the infimum I of the quantity on the right of (18): $\mathrm{S} \leq \mathrm{I}$. Let γ be any number satisfying $\mathrm{S} \leq \gamma \leq \mathrm{I}$. Set $f' = f'' = f$. Then we may rewrite (18) in the form

$$(19) \qquad -\|F\|_{\mathbf{M}} \|f + g\| \leq Ff + \gamma \leq \|F\|_{\mathbf{M}} \|f + g\|.$$

We define over **N** an extension G of F as follows: $G(f + \alpha g) = Ff + \alpha\gamma$. It is clear that G is an extension of F and that it is linear. It remains to show that $\|G\|_{\mathbf{N}} = \|F\|_{\mathbf{M}}$.

To this end we consider four cases: $\alpha = 1$; $\alpha = -1$; $\alpha > 0$; $\alpha < 0$. We prove in each case that

$$(20) \qquad |G(f + \alpha g)| = |Ff + \alpha\gamma| \leq \|F\|_{\mathbf{M}} \, \|f + \alpha g\|.$$

The inequality (19) is precisely the case $\alpha = 1$. For the case $\alpha = -1$, write $-f$ for f in (19) and multiply throughout by -1. For the case $\alpha > 0$, write f/α for f in (19) and use the homogeneous properties of the norm and of F, and similarly for $\alpha < 0$. This gives the desired extension of F to the manifold $\mathbf{N}$.

Having concluded the first stage of the proof, the extension of F by a minimal step, we turn to the general problem. If it were possible to "fill out" **B** in a finite number of steps, we could rest our case at this point. In the interesting cases with which we are principally concerned, such a finite procedure is not at hand. For these cases, use must be made of the axiom of choice, or of one of its logical equivalents, usually Zorn's lemma. Although this axiom formerly occasioned violent storms of discussion, one cannot say that the older literature indicated with exactness the precise manner in which it was applied. A sign of recent progress is the cessation of infertile discussion and the substitution of a precise formulation of its application. We propose below to present a discussion in which the anatomy of proof is completely revealed.

Consider pairs $\{\mathbf{N}, G\}$ where $\mathbf{N}$ is a linear manifold in **B** and G is a bounded linear functional defined over $\mathbf{N}$. We shall say that a pair $\{\mathbf{N}, G\}$ precedes a pair $\{\mathbf{N}', G'\}$, and we shall write

$$\{\mathbf{N}, G\} << \{\mathbf{N}', G'\}$$

if and only if $\mathbf{N} \subset \mathbf{N}'$ and G' is an admissible extension of G which in this proof implies that $\|G'\|_{\mathbf{N}'} = \|G\|_{\mathbf{N}}$. Consider now the totality T of all pairs $\{\mathbf{N}, G\}$ such that $\{\mathbf{M}, F\} << \{\mathbf{N}, G\}$, where **M** and F are as given in the theorem. This totality is partially ordered by the relation "$<<$".

Consider any totally ordered chain C in T. We represent its members by $\{\mathbf{N}_\alpha, G_\alpha\}$ where α runs over a set of indices. Let $\mathbf{N}$ be the union of the linear manifolds $\mathbf{N}_\alpha$ and let G be the bounded linear functional defined over $\mathbf{N}$ which is the "union" of the G_α

in the following sense: If $f \in \mathbf{N}$, then $f \in \mathbf{N}_\beta$ for some β and $Gf = G_\beta f$. Then for any α we have $\{\mathbf{N}_\alpha, G_\alpha\} << \{\mathbf{N}, G\}$. This means that there exists in T a pair majorizing every pair of the chain C. Applying Zorn's lemma in one of its favorite forms, we conclude that T contains a maximal element. Suppose we denote this maximal element by $\{\mathbf{P}, K\}$. Suppose that $\mathbf{P} \neq \mathbf{B}$. Then the first stage of our proof allows us to obtain an extension of K to a manifold strictly larger than $\mathbf{P}$. This contradicts the maximal character of $\{\mathbf{P}, K\}$. We conclude that $\mathbf{P} = \mathbf{B}$. This terminates the proof, the desired extension of F being the bounded linear functional K.

We now turn to a proof of the theorem in the complex case.[5]

THEOREM 6-2: *Let* $\mathbf{B}$ *be a complex Banach space and let* $\mathbf{M}$ *be a linear manifold (not necessarily closed) in* $\mathbf{B}$. *Let* F *be a complex functional defined over* $\mathbf{M}$ *which is linear and bounded.* Write $\|F\|_\mathbf{M}$ *for the bound of* F. *Then there exists a bounded linear functional* G *defined over* $\mathbf{B}$ *such that* (1) $Gf = Ff$ *for* $f \in \mathbf{M}$; (2) $\|G\| = \|F\|_\mathbf{M}$.

Proof: Any complex Banach space $\mathbf{B}$ "may be considered" to be a real space. This statement means that the set $\mathbf{B}$ has all the properties of a real Banach space if we restrict scalar multiplications to be by real scalars only. Consider, from this point of view the real linear manifold $\mathbf{M}$ mentioned in the theorem. If $f \in \mathbf{M}$ write

$$Ff = F_1 f + iF_2 f \tag{21}$$

where $F_1 f$ and $F_2 f$ are real and (21) represents the decomposition of the complex number Ff into its real and imaginary parts. It is obvious that F_1 and F_2 are functionals and it is easy to see that they are real linear; also since $|F_1 f| \leq |Ff| \leq \|F\|_\mathbf{M} \|f\|$, we have $\|F_1\|_\mathbf{M} \leq \|F\|_\mathbf{M}$.

We may obtain another decomposition of Ff into real and imaginary parts as follows: $Ff = -iF(if) = -iF_1(if) + F_2(if)$.

[5] Obtained independently by Bohnenblust and Sobczyk and by Sukhomlinov.

From this it follows that $F_2 f = -F_1(if)$ and hence (21) may be written as:

$$F f = F_1 f - iF_1(if). \tag{22}$$

Using the Hahn-Banach theorem for real spaces, we see that there exists a real bounded linear functional G_1 defined over the real space **B** which is an extension of F_1 and for which $\|G_1\| = \|F_1\|_{\mathbf{M}}$. Define a functional G over **B** by the equation: $Gf = G_1 f - iG_1(if)$. This is the functional whose existence is asserted in the theorem. One must show that: (a) $G(f + g) = Gf + Gg$; (b) $G(\alpha + i\beta)f = (\alpha + i\beta)Gf$ where α and β are real; (c) $\|G\| = \|F\|_{\mathbf{M}}$.

The proof of (a) is trivial. The proof of (b) will be set down:

$$\begin{aligned} G(\alpha + i\beta)f &= G_1(\alpha + i\beta)f - iG_1(-\beta + i\alpha)f \\ &= \alpha G_1 f + \beta G_1 if + i\beta G_1 f - i\alpha G_1 if \\ &= (\alpha + i\beta)G_1 f - i(\alpha + i\beta)G_1 if \\ &= (\alpha + i\beta)Gf. \end{aligned}$$

Toward (c), suppose that for a given f, $Gf = \gamma|Gf|$ where γ satisfies $|\gamma| = 1$ ($\gamma = \exp(i\theta)$ with θ real). Then $G(\gamma^{-1}f)$ is real, hence $G(\gamma^{-1}f) = G_1(\gamma^{-1}f)$. Thus $|Gf| = \gamma^{-1}Gf = G(\gamma^{-1}f) = G_1(\gamma^{-1}f) \leq \|G_1\|\,\|\gamma^{-1}f\| = \|G_1\|\,\|f\|$. This means that $\|G\| \leq \|G_1\| = \|F_1\|_{\mathbf{M}} \leq \|F\|_{\mathbf{M}}$ and the proof of (c) is terminated.

We now give a few applications of the Hahn-Banach theorem.

THEOREM 6-3: *Let* **B** *be a Banach space and let* $f \in \mathbf{B}$, $f \neq 0$. *Then there exists a bounded linear functional* $F \in \mathbf{B}^*$ *such that* $\|F\| = 1$ *and* $Ff = \|F\|\,\|f\|$.

On the one-dimensional subspace of **B** spanned by f (the set of all vectors of the form αf) define F by $F(\alpha f) = \alpha\|f\|$. We see that F is linear and that $\|F\| = 1$. Now F is to be extended to the whole space by the Hahn-Banach procedure.

THEOREM 6-4: *Let* **B** *be a Banach space and let* $f \in \mathbf{B}$. *Let* Φ *represent the canonical map of* **B** *into* $\mathbf{B}^{**}$ *defined by* $f \to f^{**}$ *where*

$f^{**}(F) = Ff$ with $F \in \mathbf{B}^*$. Then Φ is an isometry and an isomorphism.

We have already proved [see (17)] that Φ is a homomorphism. To prove our present theorem it is sufficient to show that $\|f^{**}\| = \|f\|$. To that end, choose $F \in \mathbf{B}^*$ so that $F \neq O$ and $Ff = \|F\| \, \|f\|$ by the previous theorem. Then we have: $\|F\| \, \|f\| = |Ff| = |f^{**}F| \leq \|f^{**}\| \, \|F\|$. Thus $\|f\| \leq \|f^{**}\|$. This inequality coupled with the more obvious $\|f^{**}\| \leq \|f\|$ gives the desired result.

THEOREM 6-5: *Let* $\mathbf{M}$ *be a closed linear manifold in* $\mathbf{B}$ *and let* g *be a vector not in* $\mathbf{M}$: $g \notin \mathbf{M}$. *Then there exists a bounded linear functional* F *such that* $Fg = 1$ *and* $Ff = 0$ *for each* $f \in \mathbf{M}$.

Proof: Let $\mathbf{N}$ be the linear manifold of all vectors of the form $f + \alpha g$ with $f \in \mathbf{M}$. Let F be the functional, over $\mathbf{N}$, defined by: $F(f + \alpha g) = \alpha$. By theorem 5-5, F is bounded and linear on $\mathbf{N}$. It may now be extended to all of $\mathbf{B}$ by the Hahn-Banach theorem.

Theorem 6-3 shows that if $f \neq O$, there exists an $F \in \mathbf{B}^*$ such that $Ff \neq 0$. Thus if $f \neq g$, there exists an F such that $Ff \neq Fg$. In other words, with the help of the Hahn-Banach theorem one may prove that there exist functionals which distinguish among pairs of elements of the space. The problem of distinguishing among linear functionals is trivial: That is, if $F \neq G$, then by definition of "$\neq$", there exists a vector f such that $Ff \neq Gf$. The two sets $\mathbf{B}$ and $\mathbf{B}^*$ are said to be *in duality* because each set distinguishes any given pair in the other.

7. Other topologies

The norm function defines a metric in the space $\mathbf{B}$ and hence defines a topology. This topology is referred to as the *strong* topology. Thus the phrase: "$\{f_n\}$ converges strongly to f" means $\|f - f_n\| \to 0$. We shall introduce below another class of topologies, the weak topologies. It is the existence of a myriad of topologies which characterizes the infinite-dimensional case. The topologies of which we shall speak now are classed as *weak*.

To give some ideas in this direction, let us introduce an expression which is useful and which has a long and distinguished past.

DEFINITION 7-1: *The sequence* $\{f_n\}$ *of vectors in* **B** *is said to converge weakly to the vector* f *providing that for every* $F \in \mathbf{B}^*$ *we have* $Ff_n \to Ff$.

Note first that we may introduce a definition: $\{f_n\}$ *converges weakly in case* $\{Ff_n\}$ *converges*—without talking about the limit vector f. Note next that if $\{f_n\}$ converges strongly to f, it also converges weakly to f. This is because

$$|Ff - Ff_n| = |F(f - f_n)| \leq \|F\| \, \|f - f_n\| \to 0.$$

It is not too difficult to give examples of sequences which converge weakly but not strongly if one has at one's disposal sufficient knowledge of the structure of specific spaces. For example, after taking up Hilbert space, such examples will be easy to find.

It will be noted that although the definition above uses topological language, *converges weakly*, there is as yet no evidence of a topology. We shall now introduce the weak topology into the space **B**, and we leave it to the reader to show that if $\{f_n\}$ converges to f in the weak topology, then $Ff_n \to Ff$ for each $F \in \mathbf{B}^*$.

Let f_0 be a fixed element of **B**. Let $\epsilon > 0$ and let $F_1, \cdots, F_n$ be elements of $\mathbf{B}^*$. Consider the set

$$\begin{aligned} \mathsf{U}(f_0) &= \mathsf{U}(f_0; F_1, \cdots . F_n, \epsilon) \\ &= \{f: |F_if - F_if_0| < \epsilon, i = 1, \cdots, n\}. \end{aligned} \tag{23}$$

The class of all sets of this type obtained by varying all the variables (including n) has certain characteristic properties: (1) $f_0 \in \mathsf{U}(f_0)$. (2) Given $\mathsf{U}(f_0)$ and $\mathsf{V}(f_0)$, there exists $\mathsf{W}(f_0)$ such that $\mathsf{W}(f_0) \subset \mathsf{U}(f_0) \cap \mathsf{V}(f_0)$. (3) If $f_1 \in \mathsf{U}(f_0)$ there exists $\mathsf{V}(f_1)$ such that $\mathsf{V}(f_1) \subset \mathsf{U}(f_0)$.

The proofs of these assertions are: (1) Trivial. (2) If $\mathsf{U}(f_0) = \mathsf{U}(f_0\colon F_1, \cdots, F_n, \epsilon)$ and $\mathsf{V}(f_0) = \mathsf{V}(f_0\colon G_1, \cdots, G_m, \delta)$ then choose $\mathsf{W}(f_0) = \mathsf{W}(f_0\colon F_1, \cdots, F_n, G_1, \cdots, G_m, \eta)$ where $\eta > 0, \eta < \epsilon, \eta < \delta$. (3) If $f_1 \in \mathsf{U}(f_0\colon F_1, \cdots, F_n, \epsilon)$, then $|\alpha_i| = |F_i f_1 - F_i f_0| < \epsilon$. Let $\delta = \epsilon - \max |\alpha_i|$. Writing $\mathsf{V}(f_1) = \mathsf{V}(f_1\colon F_1, \cdots, F_n, \delta)$ we have the desired conclusion.

The class of sets U generates a topology. The open sets of the topology are arbitrary unions of the sets U. Note that in virtue of the properties (1), (2), and (3), the finite intersection of open sets is open; the space $\mathbf{B}$ is open and so is the null set $\emptyset$. Thus we do have a topology. Note furthermore that the sets $\mathsf{U}(f_0)$ are open. Thus $\mathsf{U}(f_0)$ is a neighborhood of f_0. Indeed, the class of all sets $\mathsf{U}(f_0)$ with f_0 fixed is a base of neighborhoods of f_0 in this topology.

DEFINITION 7-2: *The topology defined by the sets* $\mathsf{U}(f_0), f_0 \in \mathbf{B}$, *is called the weak topology in* $\mathbf{B}$.

We show now that the topology is *separated* (synonyms: Hausdorff, T_2). Let $f_1, f_2 \in \mathbf{B}, f_1 \neq f_2$. By theorem 6-3, there exists an $F \in \mathbf{B}^*$ such that $Ff_1 \neq Ff_2$. Let us write $|Ff_1 - Ff_2| = 2\epsilon$. Then $\mathsf{U}(f_1\colon F, \epsilon)$ and $\mathsf{V}(f_2\colon F, \epsilon)$ are neighborhoods of f_1 and f_2 which have no points in common. This is the separation property for topologies.

The weak topology has the property that each functional $F \in \mathbf{B}^*$ is continuous (in that topology). Indeed, this topology is the weakest topology in which each such functional is continuous. This may be seen (trivially) as follows: If $f_0 \in \mathbf{B}$ and $\epsilon > 0$, then there is a neighborhood U of f_0, in fact $\mathsf{U} = \mathsf{U}(f_0\colon F, \epsilon)$, such that $f \in \mathsf{U}$ implies $|Ff - Ff_0| < \epsilon$. Hence F is continuous at f_0. Since f_0 is arbitrary, F is continuous.

The weak topology is *coarser* than the strong topology. We say also that the strong topology is *finer* than the weak. This means that any set which is open in the weak topology is open in the strong topology (the strong topology contains more open sets). This may be seen as follows: Let G be open in the weak topology. Let $f_1 \in \mathsf{G}$. Then there exists $\mathsf{U} = \mathsf{U}(f_1\colon F_1, \cdots, F_n, \epsilon)$ such that $\mathsf{U} \subset \mathsf{G}$ and $f_1 \in \mathsf{U}$. If $\delta > 0$ is sufficiently small then clearly the sphere (in the strong topology) $\{f: \|f - f_1\| < \delta\}$ lies in U. This implies that G is open in the strong topology.

We see thus that in each Banach space **B**, we may introduce a weak topology. Since $\mathbf{B}^*$ is also a Banach space, there is a weak topology in $\mathbf{B}^*$. In this case the linear functionals defining the neighborhoods of an element $F_0 \in \mathbf{B}^*$ are chosen in $\mathbf{B}^{**}$. We wish now to introduce still another topology in $\mathbf{B}^*$, the so-called *weak-star* (weak*) topology. It will be seen that the weak* topology in $\mathbf{B}^*$ is weaker (coarser) than the weak topology in $\mathbf{B}^*$.

The weak* topology is defined essentially as expected except that the functionals over $\mathbf{B}^*$ which define the neighborhoods are restricted to lie in **B**. Stated in other words, instead of choosing all of $\mathbf{B}^{**}$ as a set of functionals, we restrict ourselves to the subset in $\mathbf{B}^{**}$ which is the image under the canonical isomorphism Φ of the space **B**. It will be seen that this restriction does not affect the arguments used earlier to show that the neighborhoods (23) define a topology.

To be explicit: Let $F_0 \in \mathbf{B}^*$. Let $f_1, \cdots, f_n \in \mathbf{B}$ and let $\epsilon > 0$. Let

$$\begin{aligned} \mathsf{U} = \mathsf{U}(F_0) &= \mathsf{U}(F_0 : f_1, \cdots, f_n, \epsilon) \\ &= \{F : |Ff_i - F_0 f_i| < \epsilon, i = 1, \cdots, n\}. \end{aligned} \tag{24}$$

Then the sets U generate a topology (in which the open sets are the union of sets U) in the space $\mathbf{B}^*$. This topology is called the weak* topology. The topology is separated.

We prove now a theorem of considerable importance and which displays an essential feature of the weak* topology. The result will not be applied until later when we come to the subject of Banach algebras.

THEOREM 7-1: *The solid sphere* $\{F : \|F\| \leq 1\}$ *is a compact subset of* $\mathbf{B}^*$ *in the weak * topology.*

The proof is based on Tychonoff's theorem, and uses the elementary notion of induced topology. If $f \in \mathbf{B}$, let $\mathcal{S}_f = \{\alpha : |\alpha| \leq \|f\|\}$, it being understood that α is real or complex according as **B** is a real or complex space. Thus $\mathcal{S}_f$ is a closed segment of the real line or a closed disc of the complex plane. We shall "attach" to $\mathcal{S}_f$ the standard topology for segments and discs and we note that $\mathcal{S}_f$ is compact.

Consider now the direct product

$$\mathcal{S} = \prod_{f \in \mathbf{B}} \mathcal{S}_f \tag{25}$$

of the compact spaces $\mathcal{S}_f$. The points of $\mathcal{S}$ are the functions ϕ defined on **B** and such that $\phi(f) \in \mathcal{S}_f$. In particular, if $\phi \in \mathcal{S}$, then the scalar $\phi(f)$ is called the fth co-ordinate of ϕ. Let $F \in \mathbf{B}^*$, $\|F\| \leq 1$. Then for $f \in \mathbf{B}$, we have $|Ff| \leq \|f\|$; hence $Ff \in \mathcal{S}_f$. We see thus that functionals of the solid unit sphere in $\mathbf{B}^*$ (also called the *unit ball*) may be considered to be points of $\mathcal{S}$. If we denote this solid unit sphere by Σ, we shall write $\Sigma \subset \mathcal{S}$.

Tychonoff's theorem asserts that the space $\mathcal{S}$, "endowed" with the product topology, is compact. The product topology is the one generated by the following base of neighborhoods: Let $\phi_0 \in \mathcal{S}$ and let $f_1, \cdots, f_n \in \mathbf{B}$, $\epsilon > 0$. Then a "typical" neighborhood is the set

$$\mathsf{U}(\phi_0 : f_1, \cdots, f_n, \epsilon) = \{\phi : |\phi(f_i) - \phi_0(f_i)| < \epsilon, i = 1, \cdots, n\}.$$

It is very important for us to note here that if we consider the topology which $\mathcal{S}$ induces on Σ, then this topology is precisely the weak* topology on Σ. Having stated this critical fact, our theorem will be established providing that we show that the set Σ is a closed subset of $\mathcal{S}$. This arises from the topological theorem that a subset of a compact (separated) space is compact if and only if it is closed.

Suppose now that $\phi_0 \in \mathcal{S}$ is a limit point of Σ. Thus every neighborhood of ϕ_0 contains points of Σ. Let $\epsilon > 0$ be arbitrary and choose two vectors f and g in **B**. Consider the neighborhood $\mathsf{U} = \mathsf{U}(\phi_0 : f, g, f + g, \epsilon)$. Suppose $F \in \mathsf{U} \cap \Sigma$. Then $F(f + g) = Ff + Fg$. Also $|\phi_0(f) - Ff| < \epsilon$, $|\phi_0(g) - Fg| < \epsilon$, and $|\phi_0(f + g) -$

$F(f+g)| < \epsilon$. From this we see quickly that $|\phi_0(f+g) - \phi_0(f) - \phi_0(g)| < 3\epsilon$. Hence $\phi_0(f+g) = \phi_0(f) + \phi_0(g)$. Similarly, one proves that $\phi_0(\alpha f) = \alpha\phi_0(f)$. Finally, it is clear that $|\phi_0 f| \leq \|f\|$, hence $\|\phi_0\| \leq 1$. Thus ϕ_0 is bounded and linear, that is, it lies in Σ. This means that Σ contains all its limit points, Σ is closed, hence compact. The theorem is proved.

8. Examples and exercises

We consider now some examples of Banach spaces. We shall leave it to the reader to attempt to carry through the necessary calculations leading to the final conclusion. Some of these calculations are trivial, others can be made in reasonable time. There are still others that constitute outstanding results of the mathematical literature. We shall specify in a few cases (far from all) what the order of difficulty is. A usual rule of thumb is that, out of some ten or twelve steps that must be checked, at least eight or nine will be trivial. For a preliminary understanding of the material herein treated—enough so one can proceed to further chapters—it is necessary to be able to carry out all trivial calculations. In order to have a firm hold of the material, it is essential to carry out all calculations of intermediate difficulty. Those of outstanding talent will solve the difficult problems.

Let 1^2 be the set of all real or complex sequences $x = (x_1, x_2, \cdot \cdot \cdot)$ for which $\sum_{i=1}^{\infty} |x_i|^2 < \infty$. Scalar multiplication is to be defined in the obvious way. If $y \in 1^2$ where $y = (y_1, y_2, \cdot \cdot \cdot)$, then it may be shown (intermediate difficulty) that $x + y = (x_1 + y_1, x_2 + y_2, \cdot \cdot \cdot)$ is also in 1^2. Thus 1^2 is a vector space. Let the norm of x be defined by $\|x\| = \left(\sum_{i=1}^{\infty} |x_i|^2\right)^{1/2}$. This is indeed a norm function. With this norm, 1^2 is complete (intermediate).

It may be shown (intermediate) that if X is a bounded linear functional on $\mathbf{l}^2$, then X "is of the form"[6] $X = (X_1, X_2, \cdots)$ with $\sum_{i=1}^{\infty} |X_i|^2 < \infty$ and $Xx = \sum_{i=1}^{\infty} \bar{X}_i x_i$. Also $\|X\| = \left(\sum_{i=1}^{\infty} |X_i|^2\right)^{1/2}$. Thus if $\mathbf{B} = \mathbf{l}^2$, we may write, with seemingly good reason: $\mathbf{B} = \mathbf{B}^*$. We have here followed the convention given in (11)—for reasons which will become clear in Chapter III. Another remark: In case the space is real, the bar indicating conjugation may be omitted.

The space $\mathbf{l}^2$ is a special example of a Hilbert space. It is the original space introduced by Hilbert in his study of integral equations.

Let $\mathcal{E}$ be a set in which the notion of measure, μ, has been introduced. For example, we may consider Lebesgue measure on the real line. Let $\mathbf{L}^2 = \mathbf{L}^2(\mathcal{E}, \mu)$ be the set of measurable real- or complex-valued functions f for which $|f|^2$ is integrable—we shall write $\int_{\mathcal{E}} |f|^2 \, d\mu < \infty$. Then clearly $\alpha f \in \mathbf{L}^2$. Also (with more labor), $f + g \in \mathbf{L}^2$ when f and g do. Thus $\mathbf{L}^2$ is a vector space. Note that the function *zero* is defined by $f(x) = 0$ for each x. Let $\|f\| = \left(\int_{\mathcal{E}} |f^2| \, d\mu\right)^{1/2}$. Then $\|f\|$ so defined is not a norm function since property (2a) is not satisfied: There exist non-zero positive functions with zero integrals!

Start all over. In the set of measurable and square integrable functions, introduce an equivalence (prove) relation: $f \sim g$ in case $f(x) = g(x)$ except on a set of measure zero. Let $\mathbf{L}^2$ stand for the set of equivalence classes. In $\mathbf{L}^2$, introduce addition, scalar multiplication, norm by means of representative elements (show that this procedure is legitimate—that the functions are well defined!). Then proceed to check the axioms for a Banach space. In particular, the statement of completeness is precisely the Riesz-Fischer theorem. The space $\mathbf{L}^2$ is another example of a Hilbert space.

[6] "Is of the form" is frequently used to suggest that two types of systems are isomorphic, that is, essentially indistinguishable.

Carry out programs similar to the above for the spaces $\mathbf{l}^p$, $\mathbf{L}^p$ where $p \geq 1$ and where the spaces may be described briefly as follows: The elements in $\mathbf{l}^p$ are sequences $x = (x_1, x_2, \cdots)$ for which $\sum_{i=1}^{\infty} |x_i|^p < \infty$ with the norm defined by $\|x\| = \left(\sum_{i=1}^{\infty} |x_i|^p\right)^{1/p}$. The elements in $\mathbf{L}^p$ are equivalence classes of functions which are measurable and pth power integrable with the norm defined by $\|f\| = \left(\int_{\mathcal{E}} |f|^p \, d\mu\right)^{1/p}$.

Given the above Banach spaces, the problem of determining their adjoint spaces is one of the first magnitude. It may be shown that if $p > 1$, the adjoint of $\mathbf{l}^p$ is $\mathbf{l}^q$ where $1/p + 1/q = 1$. Similarly, the adjoint of $\mathbf{L}^p$ is $\mathbf{L}^q$. For details on this matter and for further examples of Banach spaces current in analysis, we refer the reader to Banach's book: *Théorie des opérations linéaires.*

Consider now the question of the convergence of a sequence. In the spaces $\mathbf{l}_n^p$, $p \geq 1$, it may be shown that a sequence converges strongly if and only if it converges weakly. This is due to the fact that the convergence of the co-ordinates is sufficient to ensure strong convergence. For $\mathbf{l}^2$, weak and strong convergence are not the same. Let $\{e_n\}$ be a sequence of vectors defined as follows: $e_1 = (1, 0, 0, \cdots)$, $e_2 = (0, 1, 0, \cdots)$, and so on.[7] Then $\|e_n - e_m\| = \sqrt{2}$ if $n \neq m$ and hence $\{e_n\}$ does not converge strongly. Now let $X = (X_1, X_2, \cdots)$ be any linear functional. Hence $\sum_{i=1}^{\infty} |X_i|^2 < \infty$. In particular $X_n \to 0$ as $n \to \infty$. We have: $Xe_n = X_n \to 0$ as $n \to \infty$. Thus $\{e_n\}$ converges weakly to *0*.

We shall show that in the strong topology, the unit ball of $\mathbf{l}^2$ is not compact. Keeping in mind that $\mathbf{l}^2$ is its own adjoint space (as we have discussed above), this will put in relief the difference between the strong topology and the weak* topology. Consider the denumerable set $\{\pm e_n\}$, where e_n is as in the previous para-

[7] Note that e_n in this paragraph and the next is a vector whereas x_n is the nth component of the vector x.

graph. Enumerate these vectors in some way and call them $\{a_n\}$, $n = 1, 2, \cdots$. Let $V_n = \{x : \|x - a_n\| < \sqrt{2}\}$; V_n is the *open* sphere of radius $\sqrt{2}$, center a_n. The set of spheres V_n covers the closed unit ball $\Sigma = \{x : \|x\| \leq 1\}$. For suppose $x \in \Sigma$. Write $x = (x_1, x_2, \cdots)$. (We restrict ourselves to the case in which l^2 is a real space.) We have $\sum_{i=1}^{\infty} x_i^2 \leq 1$, hence $-1 \leq x_i \leq 1$. It is clear that if for some integer m, $x_m > 0$, say, then $\|e_m - x\| < \sqrt{2}$, hence x is in one of the spheres V_n. This means that Σ is covered by the sequence of open spheres $\{V_n\}$. However no finite subcovering of Σ exists. This may be seen from the fact that $\|e_n - e_m\| = \sqrt{2}$ for $n \neq m$.

We shall show that if $\mathbf{B}$ is any Banach space, the closure in the weak* topology of the unit sphere, $S = \{F : \|F\| = 1\}$, is the unit ball $T = \{F : \|F\| \leq 1\}$. Let $F_0 \in T$, $\|F_0\| \leq 1$. Let $U(F_0) = \{F : |Ff_i - F_0 f_i| < \epsilon,\ i = 1, \cdots, n\}$ be any weak* neighborhood of F_0. We show that $U(F_0)$ intersects S. Let $\mathbf{M}$ be the linear manifold spanned by $f_1, \cdots, f_n$ and let $G \neq O$ be any linear functional such that $G \in \mathbf{M}^{\perp}$. Let α be a scalar and consider $F = F_0 + \alpha G$. Then $Ff_i - F_0 f_i = \alpha G f_i = 0$ for $i = 1, \cdots, n$. For a suitable α, $\|F\| = 1$ since $\|F_0\| \leq 1$. Thus $F \in U(F_0)$. This shows that the weak* closure of S includes T.

Now let $F_0 \notin T$. Suppose $\|F_0\| = 1 + 2\epsilon$, $\epsilon > 0$. Choose $f \in \mathbf{B}$ such that $\|f\| = 1$, $|F_0 f| > 1 + \epsilon$. Consider $U(F_0) = \{F : |Ff - F_0 f| < \epsilon\}$. If $\|G\| = 1$ we have $|F_0 f - Gf| \geq |F_0 f| - |Gf| > 1 + \epsilon - 1 = \epsilon$ and hence $G \notin U(F_0)$. This means that the weak* closure of S includes no element outside T. An alternative proof of this fact can be derived from theorem 7-1. It is clear that the proof uses the hypothesis of infinite dimensionality.

II LINEAR TRANSFORMATIONS

1. Preliminaries

Having developed the material necessary for understanding the structure of Banach spaces, we proceed to consider mappings from one Banach space to another. We consider two Banach spaces **B** and **C** of the same scalar type: both real or both complex. We are interested in mappings T from **B** into **C**. This we shall write in a variety of ways: $T:\mathbf{B} \to \mathbf{C}$; or $\mathbf{B} \xrightarrow{T} \mathbf{C}$; or $T:f \to g$, $f \in \mathbf{B}$, $g \in \mathbf{C}$; or $Tf = g$. The mappings T will usually be called *transformations*, less often *operators*. The two terms for us are synonymous. If T is a mapping from **B** into **C**, then by definition, for each $f \in \mathbf{B}$, Tf is defined and $Tf \in \mathbf{C}$. That is, the *domain* of T is **B** and the *range* of T is a subset of **C**. Later on, we shall consider mappings which are not defined on a space in its entirety. For the sake of brevity, these will also be referred to as transformations from one Banach space to another. This is the case, for example, for many operators of mathematical physics. Let us point out here that many portions of the discussion on functionals of Chapter I can be derived from the paragraphs which follow. Thus, from some points of view, we are giving a generalization of the notion of functional.

The transformations with which we deal are always *linear*, that is, they satisfy

$$T(f + g) = Tf + Tg; \tag{1a}$$

$$T(\alpha f) = \alpha(Tf). \tag{1b}$$

They will, unless expressly stated to the contrary, be bounded. This means that there exists a constant $K \geq 0$ such that for all $f \in \mathbf{B}$, $\|Tf\| \leq K\|f\|$. The least possible value of K is denoted by $\|T\|$ and is called the *bound* of T, or the *norm* of T. Thus for bounded transformations we have

$$\|Tf\| \leq \|T\| \, \|f\|. \tag{2}$$

For a bounded linear transformation we have: $\|T\| = \sup(\|Tf\|/\|f\|)$, where the supremum is taken over all $f \neq 0$. We may also limit ourselves to vectors f for which $\|f\| = 1$; also $0 < \|f\| \leq 1$. Note that there exist vectors f of norm one for which $\|Tf\|$ "almost equals" $\|T\| \, \|f\|$. The totality of bounded linear transformations from $\mathbf{B}$ into $\mathbf{C}$ will be denoted by $\mathfrak{A}(\mathbf{B}, \mathbf{C})$. In case $\mathbf{B} = \mathbf{C}$ we shall also write $\mathfrak{A}(\mathbf{B})$ for $\mathfrak{A}(\mathbf{B}, \mathbf{B})$. The transformation O defined by $Of = 0$ is linear and bounded, in fact $\|O\| = 0$. If $\mathbf{B} = \mathbf{C}$, the transformation I defined by $If = f$ is also linear and bounded; we have $\|I\| = 1$. These are the zero and identity transformations respectively. Sometimes for emphasis we may write $I_{\mathbf{B}}$. Finally, we remind the reader that since transformations are functions, $T = S$ means $Tf = Sf$ for all $f \in \mathbf{B}$.

We show now that with a suitable (and obvious) definition of addition and scalar multiplication, the set $\mathfrak{A}(\mathbf{B}, \mathbf{C})$ is a vector space.

DEFINITION 1-1: *If S and T are bounded linear transformations from* $\mathbf{B}$ *to* $\mathbf{C}$, *the transformation $S + T$ is defined by*

$$(S + T)f = Sf + Tf.$$

Similarly, αT is defined by

$$(\alpha T)f = \alpha(Tf).$$

It may be seen quickly that $S + T$ and αT are bounded linear transformations. For example (and with apologies to the reader) we have: $(S + T)(f + g) = S(f + g) + T(f + g) = (Sf + Sg) + (Tf + Tg) = (Sf + Tf) + (Sg + Tg) = (S + T)f + (S + T)g$, wherein the various equalities have various justifications. It is easily checked that $\|\alpha T\| = |\alpha|\,\|T\|$. Also, since $\|(S + T)f\| = \|Sf + Tf\| \leq \|Sf\| + \|Tf\| \leq (\|S\| + \|T\|)\|f\|$, we have $S + T$ bounded and $\|S + T\| \leq \|S\| + \|T\|$. It is also clear that $\|T\| \geq 0$ and that $\|T\| = 0$ if and only if $T = O$. We note rapidly that $T + O = T$, that $S + T = T + S$, that $S + (T + U) = (S + T) + U$; also that for a given T there exists a unique bounded linear transformation denoted by $-T$ such that $T + (-T) = O$. In other words, we have shown that the family $\mathfrak{A}(\mathbf{B}, \mathbf{C})$ is a normed vector space.

THEOREM 1-1: *The family* $\mathfrak{A}(\mathbf{B}, \mathbf{C})$ *of bounded linear transformations of* $\mathbf{B}$ *into* $\mathbf{C}$ *is a Banach space.*

Everything has been proved except completeness. The procedure is the same as that which we developed earlier in the case of linear functionals (see theorem 3-1 of Chapter I). If $\{T_n\}$ is a Cauchy sequence in $\mathfrak{A}(\mathbf{B}, \mathbf{C})$, thus $\|T_n - T_m\| \to 0$, then for some $K \geq 0$, $\|T_n\| \leq K$. We must select a candidate T to which $\{T_n\}$ converges. Since $\|T_nf - T_mf\| = \|(T_n - T_m)f\| \leq \|T_n - T_m\|\,\|f\| \to 0$, $\{T_nf\}$ is a Cauchy sequence in $\mathbf{C}$ for each $f \in \mathbf{B}$. Since $\mathbf{C}$ is complete, $\{T_nf\}$ converges to an element Tf. It must then be shown that T is bounded and linear; also that $T_n \to T$, that is, $\|T - T_n\| \to 0$. The reader should practice playing these passages until he reaches the proper tempo (presto).

We introduce

DEFINITION 1-2: *If* S *and* T *are bounded linear transformations of* $\mathbf{B}$ *into* $\mathbf{B}$, *the transformation* $S \cdot T$ *is defined by*

$$(S \cdot T)f = S(Tf).$$

If $S = T$, *we write* S^2 *instead of* $S \cdot S$.

It is easy to check that ST (the same as $S \cdot T$) is also a bounded linear transformation. (Note that, in general, multiplication of transformations is not commutative, that is $ST \neq TS$.) As for boundedness, note that since $\|(ST)f\| = \|S(Tf)\| \leq \|S\| \, \|Tf\| \leq \|S\| \, \|T\| \, \|f\|$, we have $\|ST\| \leq \|S\| \, \|T\|$.

DEFINITION 1-3: *A Banach algebra* **A** *is* (1) *a Banach space;* (2) *a ring in the sense of algebra. Furthermore, the norm function satisfies*

$$\|f \cdot g\| \leq \|f\| \cdot \|g\|.$$

To say "a ring in the sense of algebra" means that multiplication of pairs of elements has been introduced satisfying the "usual" rules of algebra (among them: associativity, distributivity, not commutativity). Banach algebras are also called *normed rings.* We see from the preceding discussion that

THEOREM 1-2: *The totality of bounded linear transformations of* **B** *into* **B** *is a Banach algebra.*

The subject of Banach algebras is taken up in Chapter VI.

Examples of linear transformations abound. The theory of matrices is a chapter in the theory of linear transformations. The spaces here are finite dimensional. The theory of linear integral equations is another chapter. The material to be developed subsequently puts us in a position to solve many types of integral equations. Linear differential operators are as a rule unbounded and can frequently be considered to be defined on a proper dense subspace of a Banach space. Consider the Hilbert space of square integrable functions f defined on the interval $0 \leq x \leq 1$. The transformation defined by $f(x) \rightarrow xf(x)$ is bounded and linear. If we consider functions defined for $-\infty < x < \infty$, the transformation is no longer bounded. The last-named transformations are prototypes of an important class which will be analyzed completely in another chapter: the self-adjoint operators.

2. The adjoint transformation

Let T be a bounded linear transformation from $\mathbf{B}$ into $\mathbf{C}$. We shall show that T induces in a natural way a transformation T^* from $\mathbf{C}^*$ into $\mathbf{B}^*$. Thus, associated with the diagram $T:\mathbf{B} \to \mathbf{C}$, we have $T^*:\mathbf{C}^* \to \mathbf{B}^*$. The transformation T^* about to be defined is called the adjoint (also dual) of T.

To this effect, let F be an arbitrary element in $\mathbf{C}^*$. The expression $F(Tf)$ where $f \in \mathbf{B}$ defines a bounded linear functional on $\mathbf{B}$. That is, there exists $G \in \mathbf{B}^*$ such that for all $f \in \mathbf{B}$, $Gf = F(Tf)$. We denote the mapping $F \to G$ by T^*. We have $T^*F = G$ and $(T^*F)f = F(Tf)$. The last identity shows that T^* is defined by a relation having associative, anti-commutative character. Let us begin to derive important properties of T^*.

THEOREM 2-1: *Let T be a bounded linear transformation from* $\mathbf{B}$ *to* $\mathbf{C}$. *Then the transformation T^*, adjoint to T, is bounded and linear from* $\mathbf{C}^*$ *to* $\mathbf{B}^*$ *and satisfies* $\|T^*\| = \|T\|$. *The transformation T^{**} is an extension of T.*

The proof of the linearity of T^* is left as an exercise. As for boundedness, note that we have $|T^*Ff| = |FTf| \leq \|F\|\,\|Tf\| \leq \|F\|\,\|T\|\,\|f\|$. Thus for any $F \in \mathbf{C}^*$, we have $\|T^*F\| \leq \|T\|\,\|F\|$. Hence T^* is bounded and, in fact, $\|T^*\| \leq \|T\|$. To prove the reverse inequality, we use consequences of the Hahn-Banach theorem (theorem 6-3 of Chapter I). For a given $f \in \mathbf{B}$, let $F \in \mathbf{C}^*$ be so chosen that $\|F\| = 1$ and $FTf = \|F\|\,\|Tf\|$. Then we have $\|F\|\,\|Tf\| = |FTf| = |T^*Ff| \leq \|T^*\|\,\|F\|\,\|f\|$. Hence $\|Tf\| \leq \|T^*\|\,\|f\|$, that is, $\|T\| \leq \|T^*\|$.

Note that T^{**} maps $\mathbf{B}^{**}$ into $\mathbf{C}^{**}$. We shall show that for $f \in \mathbf{B}$, $(Tf)^{**} = T^{**}f^{**}$ where f^{**} is the image of f under the canonical map of $\mathbf{B}$ into $\mathbf{B}^{**}$. If $F \in \mathbf{C}^*$, we have: $(T^{**}f^{**})F = f^{**}(T^*F) = (T^*F)f = F(Tf) = (Tf)^{**}F$.

We see from the preceding discussion that the passage from from T to T^* is a mapping of $\mathfrak{A}(\mathbf{B}, \mathbf{C})$ into $\mathfrak{A}(\mathbf{C}^*, \mathbf{B}^*)$. We investigate special important properties of this mapping.

THEOREM 2-2: *The adjoint mapping* $T \to T^*$ *where* $T \in \mathfrak{A}(\mathbf{B}, \mathbf{C})$ *and* $T^* \in \mathfrak{A}(\mathbf{C}^*, \mathbf{B}^*)$ *is a metric and algebraic isomorphism. That is,*

$$\begin{aligned} &\text{(a)} \quad \|T^*\| = \|T\|; \\ &\text{(b)} \quad (S + T)^* = S^* + T^*; \\ &\text{(c)} \quad (\alpha S)^* = \alpha S^*. \end{aligned}$$

In the case $\mathbf{B} = \mathbf{C}$ *we have the further identity:*

$$\text{(d)} \quad (ST)^* = T^*S^*.$$

The equality (a) has already been established. We leave (b) and (c) as exercises and look briefly at (d). If $F \in \mathbf{C}^* = \mathbf{B}^*$ and $f \in \mathbf{B}$, we have $((ST)^*F)f = F((ST)f) = F(S(Tf)) = (S^*F)(Tf) = (T^*(S^*F))f = ((T^*S^*)F)f$. Since the equality holds for all f, we have $(ST)^*F = (T^*S^*)F$. Since the latter equality holds for all F, we have $(ST)^* = T^*S^*$, which is what we wanted. The reader is advised to master the "onion peeling" technique illustrated here with two skins: the elimination, first of f, then of F.

In the case $\mathbf{B} = \mathbf{C}$ in which we deal therefore with a ring, the isomorphism of the above theorem may be referred to, more expressively, as an *anti-isomorphism.*

3. The boundedness of the inverse transformation

In order to reach a successful maturity, the abstract theory of Banach spaces needs three or so critical theorems. Once these are proved, it is possible to deploy techniques on a large scale and in a variety of directions. The first such theorem is the Hahn-Banach theorem. Its crucial value has already become apparent. The second one, to be established in this section, concerns the boundedness of the inverse transformation. Its proof depends heavily on the fact that a Banach space is complete. A dissection of the proof leads to category arguments and to classical theorems such as that a complete metric space is of the second category. The proof given below[1] yields the result rapidly at the expense of insight into the phenomena.

The problem is as follows. We have given a bounded linear transformation T from **B** into **C**. Specifically, T is a *bijection* (also called *one-to-one onto*). That is, the image of **B** under T is **C** in its entirety. And furthermore $Tf = Tg$ implies $f = g$. Under these circumstances it is clear that the inverse mapping T^{-1} exists; $T^{-1}: \mathbf{C} \to \mathbf{B}$. If $Tf_1 = g_1$ and $Tf_2 = g_2$, then $T^{-1}(g_1 + g_2) = f_1 + f_2 = T^{-1}g_1 + T^{-1}g_2$. This argument leads to the conclusion that T^{-1} is linear. It is also defined on all of **C** (by hypothesis). Question: Is T^{-1} bounded? The answer is "yes" and is formulated in

THEOREM 3-1: *Let T be a bounded linear transformation of* **B** *into* **C**. *Suppose that T is one-to-one and that its range is all of* **C**. *Then the inverse transformation T^{-1} from* **C** *into* **B** *exists, is linear, and is bounded.*

The proof will proceed by stages. If M is any set in **B**, then $T(\mathsf{M})$ will denote the set of images under T of vectors in M; $T(\mathsf{M}) = \{g : Tf = g,\ f \in \mathsf{M}\}$. We shall let the letters S and U denote spheres in **B** and **C**, in particular, $\mathsf{S}_r = \{f : \|f\| < r\}$ and $\mathsf{S}_r(f_0) = \{f : \|f - f_0\| < r\}$.

LEMMA 3-1: *For T^{-1} to be bounded, it is necessary and sufficient that there exist an $r > 0$ such that $T(\mathsf{S}_1) \supset \mathsf{U}_r$.*

If $T(\mathsf{S}_1) \supset \mathsf{U}_r$, then $T^{-1}(\mathsf{U}_r) \subset \mathsf{S}_1$ or $T^{-1}(\mathsf{U}_1) \subset \mathsf{S}_{1/r}$. This means that T^{-1} is bounded; in fact, $\|T^{-1}\| \leq 1/r$. Conversely, if T^{-1} is bounded, then for some $k > 0$, $T^{-1}(\mathsf{U}_1) \subset \mathsf{S}_k$; that is, $T(\mathsf{S}_k) \supset \mathsf{U}_1$ and $T(\mathsf{S}_1) \supset \mathsf{U}_{1/k}$.

LEMMA 3-2: *The set $T(\mathsf{S}_1)$ is dense in some sphere $\mathsf{U}_r(g)$.*

Suppose that $T(\mathsf{S}_1)$ is not dense in any sphere of **C**. Then for all $r > 0$, $T(\mathsf{S}_r)$ will not be dense in any sphere of **C**. We proceed

[1] Patterned after that given by Loomis in his *Introduction to Abstract Harmonic Analysis*, Van Nostrand, New York, 1953.

to choose a sequence of *closed* spheres $\{V^{(n)}\}$, $n = 0, 1, \cdots$, in C having radii $r_n > 0$ for which $r_n \to 0$. Let $V^{(0)}$ be arbitrary. Since $T(S_1)$ is not dense in $V^{(0)}$, there is a (closed) sphere $V^{(1)}$ such that $V^{(1)} \subset V^{(0)}$ and such that $T(S_1)$ and $V^{(1)}$ have no points in common. Since $T(S_2)$ is not dense in $V^{(1)}$, there is a sphere $V^{(2)}$ satisfying: $V^{(2)} \subset V^{(1)}$ and $T(S_2)$ and $V^{(2)}$ have no points in common. And so on for $V^{(3)}, V^{(4)}, \cdots$. These spheres have a point in common. For suppose $V^{(n)}$ has its center at g_n, then $\{g_n\}$ is a Cauchy sequence in C. Since C is complete, $g_n \to g$, say. Finally, since $V^{(n)}$ is closed, $g \in V^{(n)}$, $n = 0, 1, \cdots$. Now, since T is a bijection, there exists $f \in B$ such that $Tf = g$. If n is chosen so that $n > \|f\|$, then $f \in S_n$ and $g \in T(S_n)$. Thus $T(S_n)$ and $V^{(n)}$ have the element g in common. This contradiction shows that our hypothesis is wrong and that $T(S_1)$ *is* dense in some sphere.

LEMMA 3-3: *The set* $T(S_1)$ *is dense in a sphere* U_r *about the origin of* C.

We suppose, in accordance with the previous lemma, that $T(S_1)$ is dense in $U_r(g)$. We may assume (shrinking r slightly) that there exists a vector $f \in S_1$ such that $Tf = g$. Then the set of vectors $T(f' - f)$ where $f' \in S_1$ is dense in the sphere U_r of radius r and center at the origin (the zero element) of C. Thus $T(S_2)$ is dense in U_r and $T(S_1)$ is dense in $U_{r/2}$.

LEMMA 3-4: *The set* $T(S_1)$ *contains a sphere* U_s *about the origin of* C.

By the preceding lemma we may assume that $T(S_1)$ is dense in a sphere U_r. Let $g \in U_r$ and let $0 < \delta < 1$ (for example, one may take $\delta = \frac{1}{2}$). We shall find two sequences of elements $\{f_n\}$ and $\{g_n\}$ satisfying: $g_n \to g$; $g_n = Tf_n$; $\{f_n\}$ is convergent, say, $f_n \to f$. It will turn out that $\|f\| < (1 - \delta)^{-1}$. Since T is continuous, $Tf = g$. Thus we see that $T(S_{(1-\delta)^{-1}}) \supset U_r$. From this it is obvious that $T(S_1) \supset U_s$ where $s = r(1 - \delta)$.

Now for the definition of the sequences $\{g_n\}$ and $\{f_n\}$. Since $T(S_1)$ is dense in U_r, there exists an element $f_1 \in S_1$ such that

$g_1 = Tf_1$ satisfies $\|g_1 - g\| < r\delta$. Next, since $T(\mathsf{S}_1)$ is dense in U_r, then $T(\mathsf{S}_\delta)$ is dense in $\mathsf{U}_{r\delta}$. We may therefore say that the image under T of a sphere of radius δ with center f_1 is dense in a sphere of radius $r\delta$ with center g_1. In particular, there exists an f_2 such that $\|f_2 - f_1\| < \delta$, $\|Tf_2 - g\| < r\delta^2$. We write $g_2 = Tf_2$. At the next step, we find an f_3 such that $\|f_3 - f_2\| < \delta^2$, $g_3 = Tf_3$, and $\|g - g_3\| < r\delta^3$. The construction of our sequences $\{f_n\}$ and $\{g_n\}$ is now evident. Clearly $g_n \to g$. As for $\{f_n\}$, note that if $n > m$, then $f_n - f_m = \sum_{i=m}^{n-1} (f_{i+1} - f_i)$ and hence $\|f_n - f_m\| < \delta^m + \cdots + \delta^{n-1} < \delta^m(1 + \delta + \delta^2 + \cdots) = \delta^m(1 - \delta)^{-1}$. Thus $\{f_n\}$ is a Cauchy sequence; also since $f_n = f_1 + \sum_{i=1}^{n-1} (f_{i+1} - f_i)$, $\|f\| < (1 - \delta)^{-1}$. This completes the proof of the lemma.

The proof of theorem 3-1 is now obvious. Since $T(\mathsf{S}_1)$ contains a sphere about the origin, T^{-1} is bounded by lemma 3-1.

We give an application of the bounded inverse theorem. Consider a vector space. Suppose that it is possible to introduce into this vector space two norms, which we shall represent by $\|f\|_1$ and $\|f\|_2$, in such a way that under each of these norms the space becomes a Banach space. We shall distinguish between these two spaces by calling them $\mathbf{B}_1$ and $\mathbf{B}_2$. Suppose that in addition $\|f\|_1 \leq \|f\|_2$ for each f. Then there exists a constant $\mathrm{k} > 0$ such that $\|f\|_2 \leq \mathrm{k}\|f\|_1$. From this fact (which will be proved immediately) it follows that the topologies induced by the two norms are identical. To prove this fact consider the transformation T which carries f as an element of $\mathbf{B}_2$ onto f considered as an element of $\mathbf{B}_1$. T is a bounded bijection. Hence T^{-1} is also bounded.

A special case of the above situation will now be discussed. A Banach space $\mathbf{B}$ is said to be *finite dimensional* in case there exist vectors $b_1, \cdots, b_n$ in $\mathbf{B}$ such that if $f \in \mathbf{B}$, f is a linear combination of the b_i: $f = \alpha_1 b_1 + \cdots + \alpha_n b_n$.

Given such a set $b_1, \cdots, b_n$ it is always possible to choose a subset such that the coefficients α_i are uniquely determined. We shall assume that this is the case here. In this case, $\{b_1, \cdots, b_n\}$ is called a *basis* of **B**. It can be proved that all bases of **B** have the same number of elements. This number is called the *dimensionality* of **B**.

Let **B** be finite dimensional, of dimensionality n, and let $\{b_1, \cdots, b_n\}$ be a basis of **B**. We may and shall assume that $\|b_i\| = 1$ (if this is not the case, replace b_i by $b_i/\|b_i\|$). Consider now the space $\mathbf{l}_n^1$ introduced in Chapter I (see equation (6a)) whose vectors are n-tuples $x = (x_1, \cdots, x_n)$ with $\|x\| = |x_1| + \cdots + |x_n|$. Let us map $\mathbf{l}_n^1$ onto **B** by means of a function T defined as follows: $T(\alpha_1, \cdots, \alpha_n) = f$ where $f = \alpha_1 b_1 + \cdots + \alpha_n b_n$. Since the b_i constitute a basis, the map is properly defined; it is a bijection, and it satisfies $\|T\| \leq 1$ since $\|f\| = \|\alpha_1 b_1 + \cdots + \alpha_n b_n\| \leq |\alpha_1| + \cdots + |\alpha_n|$. By the application of the bounded inverse theorem which we considered just above, T^{-1} is bounded. Let us introduce

DEFINITION 3-1: *Two Banach spaces* **B** *and* **C** *will be said to be equivalent if there exists a bicontinuous linear bijection of* **B** *onto* **C**.

We can now state

THEOREM 3-2: *Two finite-dimensional Banach spaces* **B** *and* **C** *are equivalent if and only if they have the same dimensionality.*

If **B** and **C** both have the same dimensionality n, they are each equivalent to $\mathbf{l}_n^1$, as we have just seen, hence to each other. On the other hand, if **B** and **C** are equivalent, they have the same dimensionality since a bijection transforms a basis into a basis. Thus in the finite-dimensional case, with respect to equivalence, a Banach space is completely determined by its dimensionality.

4. Closed transformations

A most important application of the previous theorem will be considered now. The application deals with *closed* transformations. We shall give the general definition of a closed transformation at this point. In this connection, we remind the reader that although the notation $T:\mathbf{B} \to \mathbf{C}$ seems to imply that T is defined on *all* of **B**, this is not the case in sophisticated situations. Let us therefore introduce the notion of a linear transformation in its most general form.

Let Δ be a linear manifold in **B**; this implies that Δ is closed with respect to the algebraic operations of addition and scalar multiplication. We specifically exempt Δ from the requirement of being closed in the topological sense. Suppose T is a function defined on Δ and with values in a Banach space **C**. We shall say the T is a linear transformation if T satisfies conditions (1a) and (1b) on Δ. We note parenthetically, that in the applications, we shall show small interest in the cases in which Δ is not dense in **B**. We now introduce the very important notion of *closure* of a linear transformation.

DEFINITION 4-1: *Let T be a linear transformation defined on a linear manifold $\Delta \subset \mathbf{B}$. We shall say that T is closed if it has the property: Given a sequence $\{f_n\}$ such that $f_n \in \Delta$ and $f_n \to f$, $Tf_n \to g$, then $f \in \Delta$ and $Tf = g$.*

Note that all bounded transformations T defined over all of **B** are closed. For if $f_n \to f$, then obviously $\{Tf_n\}$ converges and in addition $Tf_n \to Tf$. It will be seen later that there are closed transformations which are not bounded. In particular, the unbounded self-adjoint operators in Hilbert space are closed.

We shall indicate now how the notion of closure of linear transformations is related to topological closure. Toward this end, let us define the direct product of two Banach spaces **B** and **C**. Consider the set of all ordered pairs $\{f, g\}$ where $f \in \mathbf{B}$ and $g \in \mathbf{C}$. In this set, introduce addition and scalar multiplication through the definitions:

(3a) $$\{f, g\} + \{f', g'\} = \{f + f', g + g'\};$$

(3b) $$\alpha\{f, g\} = \{\alpha f, \alpha g\}.$$

Noting that equality has the property: $\{f, g\} = \{f', g'\}$ if and only if $f = f'$ and $g = g'$, we may see that the totality of these pairs $\{f, g\}$ constitutes a vector space which is normally denoted by $\mathbf{B} \times \mathbf{C}$ and is called the *direct product* of **B** and **C**. In particular, the zero element of $\mathbf{B} \times \mathbf{C}$ is $\{0, 0\}$.

It is quite clear that $\mathbf{B} \times \mathbf{C}$ contains a subspace $\mathbf{B} \times \{0\}$ consisting of the pairs $\{f, 0]$, which is isomorphic in a natural way to **B**, and similarly for **C**. Note further that if $\{f, g\} \in \mathbf{B} \times \mathbf{C}$, then $\{f, g\} = \{f, 0\} + \{0, g\}$. Thus $\mathbf{B} \times \mathbf{C}$ is the direct sum of the manifolds $\mathbf{B} \times \{0\}$ and $\{0\} \times \mathbf{C}$. For this reason one writes frequently $\mathbf{B} \oplus \mathbf{C}$ instead of $\mathbf{B} \times \mathbf{C}$ and in fact we shall adopt this notation throughout the book.

We may introduce in $\mathbf{B} \oplus \mathbf{C}$ a norm in a variety of ways so that the resulting structure is a Banach space. For the sake of convenience, we choose the following one:

(4) $$\|\{f, g\}\| = \|f\| + \|g\|.$$

It may be seen that the function $\|\{f, g\}\|$ is a norm in fact as well as in name. It may also be seen that, in this norm, $\mathbf{B} \oplus \mathbf{C}$ is complete and hence is a Banach space. Finally (and not of immediate importance to us), it may be seen that the topology of the norm we have introduced is identical with the product topology defined in the product space.

Let us now introduce

DEFINITION 4-2: *If T is a transformation defined on a subset Δ of* **B** *into* **C**, *the graph of T is the set of pairs $\{f, Tf\}$ in $\mathbf{B} \oplus \mathbf{C}$, $f \in \Delta$.*

It is clear that if T is linear, then the graph of T is a linear manifold of $\mathbf{B} \oplus \mathbf{C}$. We now come to a theorem which explains the name "closed transformation."

THEOREM 4-1: *The graph of a linear transformation T is a closed linear manifold if and only if the transformation is closed.*

Suppose T is a closed transformation. Let $\{f_n, Tf_n\}$, $n = 1, 2, \cdots$, be the nth element of a Cauchy sequence in $\mathbf{B} \oplus \mathbf{C}$.[2] Since $\mathbf{B} \oplus \mathbf{C}$ is complete, the sequence converges to an element $\{f, g\}$. Thus $\|\{f - f_n, g - Tf_n\}\| = \|f - f_n\| + \|g - Tf_n\| \to 0$. Thus $f_n \to f$ and $Tf_n \to g$. By the definition of closed transformation, f is in the domain of T and $Tf = g$. Thus the graph is closed. The converse is similar.

We stated above that all bounded transformations (with domain $\mathbf{B}$) are closed. We are now ready to establish the converse of this proposition, a remarkable theorem. The bounded inverse theorem opens the way.

THEOREM 4-2: *Let T be a closed transformation whose domain of definition is the entire space* $\mathbf{B}$. *Then T is bounded.*

Proof: Suppose T is closed and has domain $\mathbf{B}$. Then the graph of T is a closed linear manifold $\mathbf{M}$ in the product space $\mathbf{B} \oplus \mathbf{C}$. Let us restrict to $\mathbf{M}$ the operations (algebraic and metric) defined on $\mathbf{B} \oplus \mathbf{C}$. We see in this way that $\mathbf{M}$ is a normed vector space. In fact, as a closed linear manifold in $\mathbf{B} \oplus \mathbf{C}$, $\mathbf{M}$ is complete and hence is a Banach space.

Consider the transformation S from $\mathbf{M}$ to $\mathbf{B}$ defined by $S\{f, Tf\} = f$. It is clear that S is bounded and linear. Furthermore, S is a bijection (one-to-one and onto). Thus by the bounded inverse theorem, S^{-1} is bounded. We have therefore

$$(5) \qquad \|S^{-1}f\| = \|\{f, Tf\}\| = \|f\| + \|Tf\| \leq \|S^{-1}\| \, \|f\|.$$

From this, it follows that $\|Tf\| \leq (\|S^{-1}\| - 1)\|f\|$. Thus T is bounded.

[2] In our usual notation, this would be written: $\{\{f_n, Tf_n\}\}$ is a Cauchy sequence.

5. The uniform boundedness principle

It has been pointed out in section 3 that there are some three critical theorems for Banach spaces which lead from the elementary definitions to a fruitful development. We shall prove now the last of these and give an important application of it.

THEOREM 5-1: *Let* $\{T_n\}$ *be a sequence of bounded linear transformations of* **B** *into* **C** *and for every* $f \in \mathbf{B}$, *let the sequence* $\{T_n f\}$ *be bounded. Then the sequence of norms* $\{\|T_n\|\}$ *is also bounded.*

Incidentally, the converse is obvious. If $\|T_n\| \leq \mathrm{k}$, then for a given f, $\|T_n f\| \leq \mathrm{k}\|f\|$, $n = 1, 2, \cdots$. Note also that for incomplete vector spaces, the proposition is false. Thus the argument below uses completeness in an essential way.

Moving towards a proof of the theorem, let us collect into lemmas two observations.

LEMMA 5-1: *If* T *is a bounded linear transformation, the function:* $f \to \|Tf\|$ *is continuous.*

We have for arbitrary $f_1, f_2 \in \mathbf{B}$, $f_1 = (f_1 - f_2) + f_2$, and hence $\|Tf_1\| \leq \|T(f_1 - f_2)\| + \|Tf_2\| \leq \|T\|\,\|f_1 - f_2\| + \|Tf_2\|$. Thus $\|Tf_1\| - \|Tf_2\|$ is small in absolute value when $\|f_1 - f_2\|$ is small.

LEMMA 5-2: *If there is a sphere* $\mathsf{U}_r(f_0)$ *in* **B** *of radius* $r > 0$ *and center* f_0 *such that* $\{T_n f : f \in \mathsf{U}_r(f_0),\ n = 1, 2, \cdots\}$ *is bounded, then* $\{\|T_n\|\}$ *is bounded.*

Suppose that for f in the sphere $\mathsf{U}_r(f_0)$, and for all n, $\|T_n f\| \leq \mathrm{k}$. Let g belong to the sphere U_r of radius r and center 0. Then $T_n g = T_n(g + f_0) - T_n f_0$ and hence $\|T_n g\| \leq 2\mathrm{k}$ since $g + f_0 \in \mathsf{U}_r(f_0)$. Thus $\|T_n\| \leq 2\mathrm{k}/r$.

Now, suppose that in every sphere $\mathsf{U}_r(f_0)$, the set $\{\|T_n f\|\}$, $f \in \mathsf{U}_r(f_0)$, is unbounded. We construct a nested sequence $\{\mathsf{S}^{(n)}\}$ of closed spheres, that is, a sequence satisfying $\mathsf{S}^{(0)} \supset \mathsf{S}^{(1)} \supset \cdots$.[3] We note in advance that these spheres have at

[3] For this sequence of closed spheres, no center or radius is specified.

least one point in common (the centers of the spheres form a Cauchy sequence; this is trivial if the radii converge to zero). Let $\mathsf{S}^{(0)}$ be arbitrary. By our supposition, there is a point $f_1 \in \mathsf{S}^{(0)}$ and an integer n_1, such that $\|T_{n_1}f_1\| > 1$. By lemma 5-1, there is a closed sphere $\mathsf{S}^{(1)}$ with center f_1 such that $\|T_{n_1}f\| > 1$ in all of $\mathsf{S}^{(1)}$. Returning to our supposition, there is a point $f_2 \in \mathsf{S}^{(1)}$ and an integer $n_2 > n_1$ such that $\|T_{n_2}f_2\| > 2$. Thus by lemma 5-1, $\|T_{n_2}f\| > 2$ throughout a closed sphere $\mathsf{S}^{(2)}$. Proceeding in this manner we construct the sequence of nested closed spheres $\mathsf{S}^{(r)}$ and of integers $\{n_r\}$ satisfying $n_1 < n_2 < \cdots$. Let $g \in \mathsf{S}^{(r)}$ for all r. Then $\{\|T_n g\|\}$ is not bounded since $\|T_{n_r}g\| > r$. This contradicts the hypothesis of our theorem. Thus the supposition made at the beginning of this paragraph is false. Hence by lemma 5-2, $\{\|T_n\|\}$ is bounded.

Let us note a consequence of this theorem. We see immediately that we may apply it to the case of sequences of bounded linear functionals $\{F_n\}$ since such a functional is a bounded linear transformation between two Banach spaces (**B** and the space of scalars). This leads us to the following

THEOREM 5-2: *Let* $\{f_n\}$ *be a sequence of vectors in* **B** *which is weakly convergent. That is,* $F \in \mathbf{B}^*$ *implies that* $\{Ff_n\}$ *is convergent. Then* $\{\|f_n\|\}$ *is bounded:* $\|f_n\| \leq \mathrm{k}$ *for some* $\mathrm{k} \geq 0$.

Let $F \in \mathbf{B}^*$. Note that we have $Ff_n = f_n^{**}F$ where f_n^{**} is in $\mathbf{B}^{**}$ and is the image of f under the canonical map of **B** into $\mathbf{B}^{**}$. The statement that $\{Ff_n\}$ converges implies that $\{f_n^{**}F\}$ is bounded. Thus by theorem 5-1, and invoking the remark of the preceding paragraph, $\{\|f_n^{**}\|\}$ is bounded. Since $\|f_n^{**}\| = \|f_n\|$ (by theorem 6-4 of Chapter I), we obtain the desired result.

6. Projections

We consider now the notion of projection, which notion will be basic to our entire future development. We shall examine this concept from the geometric and from the algebraic point of view.

We shall indicate briefly the basis of a calculus of projections.

Let us begin with geometric ideas. Let **B** be our background space and let **M** be a subspace of **B**. Thus **M** is a closed linear manifold in **B**. There may (and there may not) exist a closed linear manifold **N** in **B** such that **B** is the direct sum of **M** and **N**. We have introduced the notion of direct sum earlier and shall repeat it in the present context. The statement: **B** *is the direct sum of* **M** *and* **N**, *written*, $\mathbf{B} = \mathbf{M} \oplus \mathbf{N}$, means that

(6a) $\mathbf{M} \cap \mathbf{N} = \{0\};$

(6b) $f \in \mathbf{B}$ *implies* $f = g + h$ *with* $g \in \mathbf{M}$, $h \in \mathbf{N}$.

It is clear that the representation $f = g + h$ is unique. Suppose, indeed, that we have $f = g + h = g' + h'$. Then $g - g' = h' - h$. Also $g - g' \in \mathbf{M}$, $h' - h \in \mathbf{N}$. By (6a) we have $g - g' = 0$, $h' - h = 0$.

Given a pair of manifolds $\{\mathbf{M}, \mathbf{N}\}$ as above, we shall say that **N** is *complementary* to **M** (and vice versa) and that the two manifolds form a *complementary pair.*

Consider now the transformation P defined from **B** into **B** by $Pf = g$ where $f = g + h$ is the decomposition of f associated with the manifold pair $\{\mathbf{M}, \mathbf{N}\}$. Note that if $f' = g' + h'$ is the decomposition of f' then $f + f' = (g + g') + (h + h')$ is the decomposition of $f + f'$. This leads to the conclusion that P is linear.[4]

We show now that P is a closed transformation. Suppose $\{f_n\}$ is a convergent sequence, $f_n \to f$. Suppose $f_n = g_n + h_n$, $g_n \in \mathbf{M}$, $h_n \in \mathbf{N}$, and that $g_n \to g$. Then $\{h_n\}$ is convergent; let us write $h_n \to h$. Clearly $f = g + h$ where $g \in \mathbf{M}$, $h \in \mathbf{N}$. *Thus* $Pf = g$. This proves that P is a closed transformation.

Since P is closed and is defined over all of **B**, P is bounded (by theorem 4-2). Note, furthermore, that $P^2f = P(Pf) = Pg = Pf$. Thus $P^2 = P$. Transformations P such that $P^2 = P$ will be called *idempotent* transformations. Note also that **M** is precisely

[4] The pair $\{\mathbf{M}, \mathbf{N}\}$ is obviously an ordered pair. In order to lighten the language, we shall omit the participle.

the set of vectors f such that $Pf = f$; that $\mathbf{N}$ is precisely the set of vectors f such that $Pf = 0$. We recapitulate our findings in

THEOREM 6-1: *Let* $\{\mathbf{M}, \mathbf{N}\}$ *be a complementary pair of closed linear manifolds in* $\mathbf{B}$. *Thus,* $\mathbf{B}$ *is the direct sum of* $\mathbf{M}$ *and* $\mathbf{N}$, $\mathbf{B} = \mathbf{M} \oplus \mathbf{N}$. *If* $f \in \mathbf{B}$, *let* $f = g + h$, *with* $g \in \mathbf{M}$, $h \in \mathbf{N}$. *Let* P *be the transformation of* $\mathbf{B}$ *into* $\mathbf{B}$ *defined by* $Pf = g$. *Then* P *is a bounded linear transformation and* $P^2 = P$. *Furthermore, in the subspace* $\mathbf{M}$, P *is the identity transformation and in the subspace* $\mathbf{N}$, P *is the zero transformation.*

We now turn to the algebraic side of the picture. We state the results we wish to prove in

THEOREM 6-2: *Let* P *be a bounded linear idempotent* ($P^2 = P$) *transformation of* $\mathbf{B}$ *into* $\mathbf{B}$. *Let* $\mathbf{M} = \{f{:}Pf = f\}$ *and let* $\mathbf{N} = \{f{:}Pf = 0\}$. *Then the pair* $\{\mathbf{M}, \mathbf{N}\}$ *is a complementary pair of closed linear manifolds, hence* $\mathbf{B} = \mathbf{M} \oplus \mathbf{N}$. *Furthermore, the projection associated in theorem* 6-1 *to the pair* $\{\mathbf{M}, \mathbf{N}\}$ *is precisely* P.

Proof: We note that for a given $f \in \mathbf{B}$, $Pf = f$ if and only if $f = Pg$ for some g. Thus $\mathbf{M}$ is the range of the transformation P. Similarly, $Pf = 0$ if and only if $f = g - Pg$ for some g; hence $\mathbf{N}$ is the range of the transformation $I - P$. Clearly, both $\mathbf{M}$ and $\mathbf{N}$ are linear and closed. If $f \in \mathbf{M} \cap \mathbf{N}$, then $Pf = f$ and $Pf = 0$, hence $f = 0$. Finally, if f is arbitrary in $\mathbf{B}$, then $f = Pf + (f - Pf)$ and since $Pf \in \mathbf{M}$ and $f - Pf \in \mathbf{N}$, we see that $\mathbf{M} \oplus \mathbf{N} = \mathbf{B}$. The last sentence in the theorem is also clear.

DEFINITION 6-1: *A bounded linear transformation* P *satisfying* $P^2 = P$ *is called a projection. The manifold pair* $\{\mathbf{M}, \mathbf{N}\}$ *defined above is said to be associated to* P *and* P *is said to be a projection of* $\mathbf{B}$ *on* $\mathbf{M}$.

THEOREM 6-3: *Let* P *be a projection defined in* $\mathbf{B}$ *and let* $\{\mathbf{M}, \mathbf{N}\}$ *be the associated manifold pair. Let* P^* *be the adjoint of* P. *Then* P^*

is a projection defined in $\mathbf{B}^*$. *If* $\{\mathbf{M}^*, \mathbf{N}^*\}$ *is the manifold pair associated to* P^*, *then* $\mathbf{M}^* = \mathbf{N}^\perp$ *and* $\mathbf{N}^* = \mathbf{M}^\perp$.

Since $P^2 = P$, $(P^2)^* = P^*$. But $(P^2)^* = (P \cdot P)^* = P^*P^*$, hence $(P^*)^2 = P^*$ and P^* is a projection.

Let $F \in \mathbf{M}^*$; thus $P^*F = F$. If $f \in \mathbf{N}$, then $Ff = (P^*F)f = F(Pf) = F0 = 0$. Thus $F \perp \mathbf{N}$. Hence $\mathbf{N}^\perp \supset \mathbf{M}^*$. (We remind the reader that $\mathbf{N}^\perp = \{F : Ff = 0,\ f \in \mathbf{N}\}$.) Now suppose $F \in \mathbf{N}^\perp$. Write $f = g + h$, $g \in \mathbf{M}$, $h \in \mathbf{N}$. Then $(P^*F)f = F(Pf) = Fg = F(g + h) = Ff$. Thus $P^*F = F$. This means that $\mathbf{N}^\perp \subset \mathbf{M}^*$. Thus finally $\mathbf{M}^* = \mathbf{N}^\perp$. The proof of the equation $\mathbf{N}^* = \mathbf{M}^\perp$ is similar.

Note that if P is a projection associated to the pair $\{\mathbf{M}, \mathbf{N}\}$, then $I - P$ is a projection associated to the pair $\{\mathbf{N}, \mathbf{M}\}$. If P_1 and P_2 are projections which commute ($P_1P_2 = P_2P_1$) then P_1P_2 is a projection (since $(P_1P_2)^2 = P_1P_2$). Also $P_1 + P_2 - P_1P_2$ is a projection (prove by squaring). Also $P_1 + P_2 - 2P_1P_2$ is a projection. We leave it to the reader to carry out the interesting calculation of determining the associated pairs of linear manifolds in each case.

Suppose that P_1 and P_2 are projections. Suppose $\mathbf{M}_1 \supset \mathbf{M}_2$ and $\mathbf{N}_1 \subset \mathbf{N}_2$. For this case we shall write $P_1 \succ P_2$. It is clear that the relation "$\succ$" introduces a partial ordering[5] in the set of all projections (acting on $\mathbf{B}$). It is also clear that if $P_1 \succ P_2$, then $P_1P_2 = P_2$ and $P_2P_1 = P_2$; hence P_1 and P_2 commute. Conversely, if $P_1P_2 = P_2P_1 = P_2$, then $P_1 \succ P_2$.

The experienced reader will see, therefore, that a proper setting for the study of sets of commutative projections is that of Boolean algebras. We shall deal heavily later on with sets of commutative projections. However, we shall nowhere appeal to the language and operations of Boolean algebras in our development.

Let us consider now a most important reason for the introduction of the notion of projection. Let T be a bounded linear transformation of $\mathbf{B}$ into itself: $T \in \mathfrak{A}(\mathbf{B})$. A fundamental—and

[5] A binary relation "$\succ$" introduces a partial ordering in a set S providing that: $a \succ a$ for all $a \in S$; $a \succ b$ and $b \succ c$ implies $a \succ c$; $a \succ b$ and $b \succ a$ implies $a = b$. As usual, one writes at will $b \prec a$ instead of $a \succ b$.

as yet unsolved—problem of functional analysis is that of obtaining complete information on the structure of T—whatever that means. We shall not attempt to say all that this might mean, but we shall suggest some of the things that are involved.

If one considers an arbitrary linear manifold $\mathbf{M}$, then the image of $\mathbf{M}$ under T is usually located in some part of the space $\mathbf{B}$ which has no evident relation to $\mathbf{M}$. There are cases though in which this image, which we shall denote by T(M), lies in $\mathbf{M}$. This situation is very important for in this case T restricted to $\mathbf{M}$ gives a transformation which carries $\mathbf{M}$ into itself. Suppose that the situation is even more special. Let $\{\mathbf{M}, \mathbf{N}\}$ be a complementary pair of closed linear manifolds and suppose $T(\mathbf{M}) \subset \mathbf{M}$ and $T(\mathbf{N}) \subset \mathbf{N}$. Then the transformation T over $\mathbf{B}$ "splits" into two parts: T restricted to $\mathbf{M}$ and T restricted to $\mathbf{N}$. Since T is linear and since every vector is the unique sum of a vector in $\mathbf{M}$ and one in $\mathbf{N}$, the structure of T is completely known if it is known on each of $\mathbf{M}$ and $\mathbf{N}$. This splitting process is tremendously important in the study of linear transformations since it replaces one large space by two smaller spaces. Let us introduce the process formally.

DEFINITION 6-2: *Let* $\{\mathbf{M}, \mathbf{N}\}$ *be a complementary pair of closed linear manifolds and let* T *be a bounded linear transformation. Suppose* $T(\mathbf{M}) \subset \mathbf{M}$ *and* $T(\mathbf{N}) \subset \mathbf{N}$. *In this case the pair* $\{\mathbf{M}, \mathbf{N}\}$ *is said to reduce* T.

We give below the cardinal relation between reducibility and projections.

THEOREM 6-4: *Let* $\{\mathbf{M}, \mathbf{N}\}$ *be a complementary pair of linear manifolds and let* P *be their associated projection. Let* T *be a bounded linear transformation. Then* $\{\mathbf{M}, \mathbf{N}\}$ *reduces* T *if and only if*

$$TP = PT. \tag{7}$$

Proof: Assume that $\{\mathbf{M}, \mathbf{N}\}$ reduces T. Let $g \in \mathbf{M}$. Then $Pg = g$ and since $Tg \in \mathbf{M}$, $PTg = Tg$. Thus $TPg = PTg$, similarly, if

$h \in \mathbf{N}$, $Ph = 0$ and $PTh = 0$. Thus $TPh = PTh$. By linearity, (7) holds for an arbitrary $f \in \mathbf{B}$.

Suppose now that (7) holds. Then if $g \in \mathbf{M}$, $Tg = TPg = PTg$ showing that $Tg \in \mathbf{M}$. Similarly if $h \in \mathbf{N}$, $0 = TPh = PTh$, hence $Th \in \mathbf{N}$.

The significance of this theorem is the following. In order to obtain information on the structure of T it would seem necessary to determine the class of all projections which commute with T; if not of all, at least of a substantial part. This is precisely the program which we shall follow later on. In particular, we shall seek projections which are "functions" of T (for example, it is conceivable that T^3 is a projection). For functions of T—suitably defined—it will not be necessary to worry much about the commutativity with T since that should be automatic for any function. We shall see later that for an arbitrary T it is possible to define analytic functions. For special situations we can even define continuous and measurable functions.

7. Topologies for transformations

If **B** and **C** are Banach spaces, we have seen that the family $\mathfrak{A}(\mathbf{B}, \mathbf{C})$ of all bounded linear transformations of **B** into **C** is a Banach space. There is thus defined $\mathfrak{A}(\mathbf{B}, \mathbf{C})$ a topology, that of the norm. This topology is called the *uniform* topology. Being a metric topology it is by all odds the simplest in $\mathfrak{A}(\mathbf{B}, \mathbf{C})$ and results that can be established in its context should undoubtedly be so derived rather than referred to more complicated topologies.

DEFINITION 7-1: *The uniform topology in the Banach space* $\mathfrak{A}(\mathbf{B}, \mathbf{C})$ *is the topology defined by the norm.*

There are two other topologies in $\mathfrak{A}(\mathbf{B}, \mathbf{C})$ which receive frequent attention: the *strong* topology and the *weak* topology. We introduce these below. However, instead of doing so properly, we introduce some phrases which are used frequently and on the basis of which the topologies may be reconstructed explicitly.

DEFINITION 7-2: *Let* $\{T_n\}$ *be a sequence in* $\mathfrak{A}(\mathbf{B}, \mathbf{C})$ *and let* $T \in \mathfrak{A}(\mathbf{B}, \mathbf{C})$. *Suppose that for every* $f \in \mathbf{B}$, $\|Tf - T_nf\| \to 0$. *Then* $\{T_n\}$ *is said to converge strongly to* T.

DEFINITION 7-3: *Let* $\{T_n\}$ *be a sequence in* $\mathfrak{A}(\mathbf{B}, \mathbf{C})$ *and let* $T \in \mathfrak{A}(\mathbf{B}, \mathbf{C})$. *Suppose that for every* $f \in \mathbf{B}$, $F \in \mathbf{C}^*$, $|FTf - FT_nf| \to 0$. *Then* T_n *is said to converge weakly to* T.

Clearly, uniform convergence implies strong convergence; and strong convergence implies weak convergence. Now for a few words about the proper definition of the topologies. (Incidentally, the above definitions suffice for any development which we contemplate.) For the strong topology, a neighborhood of T_0 (better: a member of a base of neighborhoods), determined by an $\epsilon > 0$ and vectors $f_1, \cdots, f_n$, is: $\mathsf{U}(T_0; f_1, \cdots, f_n, \epsilon) = \{T: \|Tf_i - T_0f_i\| < \epsilon, i = 1, \cdots, n\}$. For the weak topology one considers as members of a base of neighborhoods of T_0, sets of the form $\{T: |F_i(Tf_j - T_0f_j)| < \epsilon, i = 1, \cdots, n, j = 1, \cdots, m\}$ where the F_i and f_j are appropriately chosen.

8. On range and null-space

If T is a bounded linear transformation the *null-space* of T is the set of vectors f such that $Tf = 0$. Let us call it $\mathbf{N}$. Thus $\mathbf{N} = \{f: Tf = 0\}$. It is clear that $\mathbf{N}$ is a closed linear manifold. By the *range* of T is meant the set of vectors g of the form $g = Tf, f \in \mathbf{B}$. Clearly the range is a linear manifold. However, it need not be closed. Let $\mathbf{R}$ represent the closure of the range. For projections we have seen that $\{\mathbf{N}, \mathbf{R}\}$ is a complementary pair of manifolds in the space $\mathbf{B}$. For transformations $T \in \mathfrak{A}(\mathbf{B})$, it is in general false that $\mathbf{N} \cap \mathbf{R} = \{0\}$ and also that $\mathbf{N}$ and $\mathbf{R}$ span $\mathbf{B}$.

Let T^* represent the adjoint of $T(T^* \in \mathfrak{A}(\mathbf{B}^*)$ and let $\mathbf{N}^*$ and $\mathbf{R}^*$ represent respectively the null space and the closure of the range of T^*. The question arises whether there are relations among $\mathbf{N}$, $\mathbf{R}$, $\mathbf{N}^*$, $\mathbf{R}^*$ such as those specified in theorem 6-3.

The fact is that if the space **B** is reflexive, a complete set of relations of the desired type exists. Indeed the existence of these relations for reflexive spaces heavily underlines the importance of reflexivity in the study of the structure of transformations. Without further generalities, let us enunciate[6]

THEOREM 8-1: *Let* **B** *be a reflexive space and let* $T \in \mathfrak{A}(\mathbf{B})$. *Let* **N** *and* R *denote the null-space of* T *and the closure of the range of* T. *Let* T^*, $\mathbf{N}^*$, *and* $\mathbf{R}^*$ *be the corresponding structures defined in the space* $\mathbf{B}^*$. *Then*

$$\text{(8a)} \qquad \mathbf{N}^{\perp} = \mathbf{R}^*, \qquad \mathrm{R}^{\perp} = \mathbf{N}^*.$$

$$\text{(8b)} \qquad \mathbf{N}^{*\perp} = \mathrm{R}, \qquad \mathbf{R}^{*\perp} = \mathbf{N}.$$

We note that $\mathbf{B}^*$ is reflexive. Also, we shall consider $\mathbf{B}^{**}$ to be identical with **B**. Since T^{**} is an extension of T (by theorem 2-1), for reflexive spaces, $T^{**} = T$. We have therefore that $\mathbf{N}^{**} = \mathbf{N}$ and $\mathrm{R}^{**} = \mathrm{R}$. The upshot of these comments is that we need not prove the statements in (8b) since their conclusions are contained in (8a).

The proof of each equality in (8a) is obtained—as usual—by establishing a double inclusion. To start off, let $F \in \mathbf{N}^*$. Thus $T^*F = O$. Now, if $f \in \mathbf{B}$, $0 = (T^*F)f = F(Tf)$. Thus F is orthogonal to the range of T and (by continuity) to the closure R of the range of T. This means that $\mathbf{N}^* \subset \mathrm{R}^{\perp}$. Now suppose $F \in \mathrm{R}^{\perp}$. Then for all $f \in \mathbf{B}$, $F(Tf) = 0$. But $F(Tf) = (T^*F)f$. Hence $T^*F = O$ and $F \in \mathbf{N}^*$. Thus $\mathrm{R}^{\perp} \subset \mathbf{N}^*$. In consequence we have $\mathrm{R}^{\perp} = \mathbf{N}^*$. (Note that the assumption of reflexivity has not been used.)

Now let F be arbitrary in $\mathbf{B}^*$ and let $T^*F = G$. If $f \in \mathbf{N}$, then $Gf = (T^*F)f = F(Tf) = 0$. Thus G is orthogonal to **N**. This means that $\mathbf{N}^{\perp} \supset \mathrm{R}^*$ (use the fact that $\mathbf{N}^{\perp}$ is closed). Now suppose that $\mathbf{N}^{\perp} \neq \mathrm{R}^*$. Let $F \in \mathbf{N}^{\perp}$, $F \notin \mathrm{R}^*$. Then there exists a functional in $\mathbf{B}^{**}$ which is 0 on R^* and is 1 on F (by theorem 6-5 of Chapter I). Since **B** is reflexive, we have the existence of

[6] Given by the author in 1939.

an $f \in \mathbf{B}$ such that $f \perp \mathbf{R}^*$, $Ff = 1$. Since $f \perp \mathbf{R}^*$, $(T^*G)f = 0$ for all $G \in \mathbf{B}^*$. Hence $G(Tf) = 0$ for all G, thus $Tf = 0$. This means that $f \in \mathbf{N}$ and since $F \in \mathbf{N}^\perp$, $Ff = 0$. This contradicts $Ff = 1$. Thus the hypothesis that $\mathbf{N}^\perp \neq \mathbf{R}^*$ is false. The theorem is proved.

An important application of this theorem will be given in the next section.

9. The mean-ergodic theorem

We shall not be concerned with the historical origins of this theorem. Our aim will be to present an "abstract" ergodic theorem. From this, the (discrete) concrete case can be obtained in a few brief strokes. A further word about the word "mean" which has topological significance. If $\{f_n\}$ is a sequence of functions, we have (among others) three important types of convergence to a limit function f: (1) Pointwise convergence, meaning $f_n(x) \to f(x)$ for each x. (2) Convergence almost everywhere, meaning $f_n(x) \to f(x)$ except on a set of measure zero. (3) Convergence in the mean of order $p \geq 1$, meaning $\int |f(x) - f_n(x)|^p \, dx \to 0$. In Banach spaces of functions, the norm is frequently given by integrals such as the above. Thus "convergence in the mean" can be translated into "strong convergence." Note that, above, (1) implies (2) implies (3). Thus a proof of convergence in the mean is not as strong as a proof in the sense of (2) or (1).

The mean-ergodic theorem was originally proved by von Neumann for unitary operators in Hilbert space. His proof was simplified and skeletonized by F. Riesz. In essentially this simplified form we have extended the proof to reflexive spaces. The critical element of the proof is the theorem of the preceding section relating the null space and range of T and T^*. We shall now enunciate the theorem.

THEOREM 9-1: *Let* $\mathbf{B}$ *be a reflexive space and let* V *be a uniformly bounded transformation of* $\mathbf{B}$ *into itself, that is,* $\|V^n\| \leq \mathrm{k}$, $n = 0,$

1, 2, $\cdots$.[7] *Let T_n be the transformation defined by*

$$T_n = n^{-1}(I + V + V^2 + \cdots + V^{n-1}).$$

Then the sequence $\{T_n\}$ converges strongly to a projection P for which $\|P\| \leq$ k. Let **N** *be the null space of $I - V$ and let* R *be the closure of the range of $I - V$. Then* **N**, R *is a complementary pair of manifolds and the projection associated to the pair is P.*

Let us start off with a miscellany of observations. First of all, $\mathbf{N} = \{f : Vf = f\}$; R is the closure of $\{f : f = g - Vg,\ g \in \mathbf{B}\}$. Also, V^* is uniformly bounded since $\|(V^*)^n\| = \|(V^n)^*\| = \|V^n\| \leq$ k, $n = 0, 1, \cdots$. Furthermore, $T_n^* = n^{-1}(I^* + V^* + \cdots + (V^*)^{n-1})$. Also, by the theorem of the preceding section (theorem 8-1), $\mathrm{R}^\perp$ is the null-space of the transformation $(I - V)^* = I^* - V^*$; and $\mathbf{N}^\perp$ is the closure of the range of $I^* - V^*$. We write $\mathbf{N}^* = \mathrm{R}^\perp$ and $\mathrm{R}^* = \mathbf{N}^\perp$.

Suppose now that $f \in \mathbf{N}$; thus $Vf = f$. Then $V^n f = f$, $n = 1, 2, \cdots$, and $T_n f = f$. Thus on **N**, $T_n f \to f$. Now let $f \in \mathrm{R}$. This means that for $\epsilon > 0$, there exist two vectors g and h such that $f = g - Vg + h$ where $\|h\| < \epsilon$. An easy calculation shows that $T_n f = n^{-1}(g - V^n g + h + Vh + \cdots + V^{n-1}h)$. Keeping in mind that $\|V^r\| \leq$ k, we see that (remembering that k $\geq$ 1)

$$\|T_n f\| \leq 2n^{-1}\mathrm{k}\|g\| + \mathrm{k}\epsilon.$$

It is now clear that $f \in \mathrm{R}$ implies that $T_n f \to 0$.

The above argument shows that $\mathbf{N} \cap \mathrm{R} = \{0\}$. Suppose $f_1 \in \mathbf{N}$ and $f_2 \in \mathrm{R}$. Then $T_n(f_1 + f_2) \to f_1$. Since $\|T_n\| \leq$ k, $\|f_1\| \leq \mathrm{k}\|f_1 + f_2\|$. We have therefore shown that $\{T_n\}$, restricted to vectors in $\mathbf{N} \oplus \mathrm{R}$, converges to a projection P on **N** for which $\|P\| \leq$ k. It remains to show that $\mathbf{N} \oplus \mathrm{R} = \mathbf{B}$.

By virtue of our preliminary remarks, we see that T_n^*, restricted to the manifold $\mathbf{N}^* \oplus \mathrm{R}^*$, converges to a projection on $\mathbf{N}^*$. In particular $\mathbf{N}^* \cap \mathrm{R}^* = \{0\}$. Now suppose there is an $f \neq 0$ such that $f \notin \mathbf{N} \oplus \mathrm{R}$. Then there exists an $F \in \mathbf{B}^*$ such that

[7] We remind the reader that by definition, $V^0 = I$.

$F \perp \mathbf{N} \oplus \mathrm{R}$ and $Ff = 1$; hence $F \neq O$. But $F \in \mathbf{N}^{\perp} = \mathrm{R}^*$ and $F \in \mathrm{R}^{\perp} = \mathbf{N}^*$. Hence $F = O$. This contradiction shows that $\mathbf{N} \oplus \mathbf{R} = \mathbf{B}$. The theorem is proved.

A few brief paragraphs indicating how this abstract ergodic theorem applies to "phenomena of physics." Let Ω be a space in which a measure μ is defined and let us suppose $\mu(\Omega) < \infty$. Let $\mathfrak{J}$ be a measure-preserving transformation over Ω. Let $\mathbf{L}^2_\Omega$ be the Hilbert space of square integrable μ-measurable functions. If $f \in \mathbf{L}^2_\Omega$ let $g = Vf$ where $g(x) = f(\mathfrak{J}x)$. Then $\|V\| = 1$ and $\|V^n\| = 1$. Since Hilbert space is reflexive we may apply our previous theorem to show that $n^{-1}(I + V + \cdots + V^{n-1}) \to P$ strongly.

Now suppose $\mathfrak{J}$ is *metrically transitive*. This means that if Σ is a measurable subset of Ω for which $\mathfrak{J}(\Sigma) = \Sigma$ up to sets of measure zero, then $\Sigma = \Omega$ or $\Sigma = \emptyset$, up to sets of measure zero. Note that constant functions are in $\mathbf{L}^2_\Omega$ and that if f is a constant function, $Pf = f$ since $Vf = f$. It is easy to show that with metrical transitivity, the manifold $\mathbf{N}$ is one dimensional and consists only of constant functions.

Let Σ be a measurable subset of Ω. Let f be the characteristic function of Σ. Thus $\int f\, d\mu = \mu(\Sigma)$, the measure of Σ, and $\int T_n f\, d\mu = \mu(\Sigma)$. Since $T_n f$ converges to a constant c, $T_n f \to c$, we see by integration that $\mu(\Sigma) \to c\mu(\Omega)$ and hence $c = \mu(\Sigma)/\mu(\Omega)$. This quantity is called the space mean of Σ. On the other hand, the number $T_n f(x)$ represents the proportion of "time" that under $\mathfrak{J}$ and its iterates, x spends in Σ.[8] Thus the ergodic theorem states that in the metrically transitive case (keeping in mind that we have convergence in the mean, which is not even convergence almost everywhere) the time mean of a point x measured relative to Σ converges to the space mean of Σ.

[8] The definition of characteristic function implies that $f(x) = 1$ if $x \in \Sigma$, $f(x) = 0$ otherwise. Writing $x_0 = x$, $x_1 = \mathfrak{J}(x)$, $x_2 = \mathfrak{J}(\mathfrak{J}(x))$, $\cdots$, we see that the integer $f(x_0) + \cdots + f(x_{n-1}) = (I + V + \cdots + V^{n-1})f(x)$ represents the number of times x and its transforms visit Σ in n "attempts" and $T_n f(x)$ represents the fraction of time that is spent in Σ.

III HILBERT SPACE

1. Definition

This chapter is dedicated to Hilbert space. The role of Hilbert space among all Banach spaces is exceptional. The space is unique and it seems to know it. The reader should note the extraordinary concision, harmony, and beauty of the concepts and proofs in this field. Certain it is that of all spaces, Hilbert space presents the greatest orderliness and the greatest plenitude of results.

The fundamental reason for the special position of this space arises from the fact that it is self-adjoint, that is, $\mathbf{H}^* = \mathbf{H}$. We shall indicate later the precise meaning which is to be given to this statement. However, we may see in advance (at any rate for real spaces) that this should imply that if f and $g \in \mathbf{H}$, then either f or g may act as linear functional on the other. Thus the function fg is bilinear in both arguments. Also a correct interpretation of $\mathbf{H}^* = \mathbf{H}$ implies that $ff = \|f\|^2$. The quantity which we have been writing as fg out of habit from the functional notation Fg of the previous chapters is usually written as (f, g) or $(f \mid g)$. It is read: the *inner product* of f and g (*also the scalar product*). Let us introduce our first definition.

DEFINITION 1-1: *A real or complex vector space* $\mathbf{H}$ *is called an inner-product space (also pre-Hilbert space) if there is defined a real- or complex-valued function of pairs of vectors* f, g *in* $\mathbf{H}$ *and denoted by* (f, g) *(also by* $(f \mid g)$*). This function satisfies the following conditions:*

(1a) $(f_1 + f_2, g) = (f_1, g) + (f_2, g);$

(1b) $(\lambda f, g) = \lambda(f, g);$

(1c) $(g, f) = \overline{(f, g)};$

(1d) $(f, f) \geq 0;\ (f, f) = 0$ *if and only if* $f = 0$.

Some remarks. By (1a) and (1b), the function is linear in the first variable. Since $(f, g_1 + g_2) = \overline{(g_1 + g_2, f)} = \overline{(g_1, f)} + \overline{(g_2, f)} = (f, g_1) + (f, g_2)$, we see that the function is additive with respect to the second variable. (Note that $\overline{(f, g)}$ represents the complex conjugate of $(f\ g)$. In particular if **H** is a real vector space, $\overline{(f, g)} = (f, g)$ and we may drop the "bar.") Next, we have $(f, \lambda g) = \overline{(\lambda g, f)} = \bar{\lambda}\overline{(g, f)} = \bar{\lambda}(f, g)$. Thus the inner-product function is semilinear in the second variable. For these reasons the function (f, g) is sometimes called a *sesquilinear form*. More frequently it is called a *Hermitian bilinear form*. In particular, by virtue of (1d) the form is *positive* (better called: *strictly positive*). In other words: A pre-Hilbert space is a structure consisting of a vector space **H** and a strictly positive Hermitian bilinear form defined on $\mathbf{H} \times \mathbf{H}$ to the field of scalars.

Write $\|f\|$ for $(f, f)^{1/2}$. Then we have $\|f\| \geq 0$; $\|f\| = 0$ if and only if $f = 0$. Also by (1b) and (1c), $(\lambda f, \lambda f) = \lambda(f, \lambda f) = \lambda \cdot \bar{\lambda}(f, f)$ and hence $\|\lambda f\| = |\lambda|\ \|f\|$. This suggests that the real-valued function $f \rightarrow \|f\|$ defined on **H** is a norm. We shall show presently that the triangle inequality is satisfied and hence that we do have a norm. To this end we establish a theorem known as the *Schwarz Inequality*.

THEOREM 1-1: *For any vectors* f, g

(2) $$|(f, g)| \leq \|f\|\ \|g\|.$$

The equality holds if and only if f *and* g *are linearly dependent: there exist* λ, μ, *not both zero, such that* $\lambda f + \mu g = 0$.

First, suppose **H** is a real space. If $f = 0$, then $f = 0 \cdot f$ and by (1b), $(f, g) = 0$. In this case (2) is satisfied. Suppose now $f \neq 0$. Then for any λ, we have

$$(3) \quad 0 \leq (\lambda f + g, \lambda f + g) = \lambda^2(f, f) + 2\lambda(f, g) + (g, g).$$

(In "expanding" the expression $(\lambda f + g, \lambda f + g)$ we have used the bilinearity of the inner product and the fact that $(f, g) = (g, f)$ since **H** is real.) Setting in (3) the value $\lambda = -(f, g)/\|f\|^2$, we have

$$\|f\|^{-2}(-(f, g)^2 + \|f\|^2 \|g\|^2) \geq 0.$$

This yields the Schwarz Inequality (2). The case of equality mentioned in the theorem is left as an exercise.

This disposes of the real case. Now suppose **H** is complex and for a pair of vectors f, g, suppose $(f, g) = \exp(i\theta) |(f, g)|$ where θ is real and where, of course, $|\exp(i\theta)| = 1$. Let $f' = \exp(-i\theta)f$. Then $(f', g) = |(f, g)|$. Since (f', g) is a real quantity, the argument of the last paragraph applies and we see that $(f', g) \leq \|f'\| \|g\|$. Since $\|f\| = \|f'\|$, the proof of (2) follows.

We are now in a position to prove the triangle inequality for the norm.

THEOREM 1-2: *For any vectors f and g in* **H**, *we have*

$$(4) \qquad \|f + g\| \leq \|f\| + \|g\|.$$

For a complex number α, one writes $\mathcal{R}(\alpha)$ and $\mathcal{I}(\alpha)$ to represent the real and the imaginary parts of α. We have: $(f + g, f + g) = \|f\|^2 + (f, g) + (g, f) + \|g\|^2 = \|f\|^2 + 2\mathcal{R}(f, g) + \|g\|^2 \leq \|f\|^2 + 2|(f, g)| + \|g\|^2 \leq \|f\|^2 + 2\|f\| \|g\| + \|g\|^2 = (\|f\| + \|g\|)^2$. This gives the inequality (4). We leave to the reader the interesting case of equality.

We see therefore that the quantity $\|f\|$ has all the properties of a norm and that **H** may be considered a normed space. The space may or may not be complete in this norm. This situation leads to

DEFINITION 1-2: *A complete inner-product space is called a Hilbert space.*

We mention in passing the following. If an inner-product space is not complete, it may, like any other metric space, be embedded in a complete space. Question: Can the inner product be extended (in a satisfactory manner) to this complete space? The answer is "yes." The phrase "satisfactory manner" covers a big list of desiderata. It is a good exercise in incisive thinking to enumerate them.

We make another remark. We shall associate later a dimension to each Hilbert space. This dimension is a cardinal number. The spaces of finite dimensionality are also called *Euclidean* spaces. Historically speaking, the name "Hilbert space" has been reserved for those of denumerable (infinite) dimensionality. These latter and the finite-dimensional spaces form precisely the class of separable Hilbert spaces. We see thus that the spaces divide into three classes: the finite-dimensional, the infinite-dimensional separable, and the non-separable (which are automatically infinite dimensional).

We may expect to find reproduced in Hilbert spaces the multitude of classical phenomena which we find in elementary Euclidean geometry. Of these various classical theorems, we shall prove here only one: the *parallelogram identity*. This result states that the squares of the lengths of the four sides of a parallelogram and the squares of the lengths of the two diagonals have equal sums.

THEOREM 1-3: *If f and g are arbitrary vectors in a Hilbert space* **H**, *then*

$$\|f + g\|^2 + \|f - g\|^2 = 2\|f\|^2 + 2\|g\|^2. \tag{5}$$

Proof: $\|f + g\|^2 = (f + g, f + g) = (f, f) + (f, g) + (g, f) + (g, g) = \|f\|^2 + \|g\|^2 + (f, g) + (g, f)$. The rest is obvious.

It is interesting to note that the parallelogram identity characterizes Hilbert space. That is, let **B** be a Banach space for which the norm satisfies (5) for every pair of vectors f and g. Then an inner product may be introduced in **B** whose derived norm is precisely the norm given at the start. One may even go beyond this. Let **B** be a Banach space and let $F(x, y, u, v)$ be a (non-trivial) function of four variables such that for $x = \|f\|$, $y = \|g\|$, $u = \|f + g\|$, $v = \|f - g\|$, $F(x, y, u, v) = 0$. Then, as before, an inner product may be introduced in **B** "making it" a Hilbert space.

Let us now consider rapidly some examples of Hilbert spaces. For a fixed positive n, consider the vector space of n-tuples $x = (x_1, \cdots, x_n)$ where the x_i are scalars. Introduce an inner product as follows: If $y = (y_1 \cdots, y_n)$, then $(x, y) = \sum_{i=1}^{n} x_i\overline{y_i}$. (That this is an inner product, and hence satisfies (1), may be checked immediately.) The norm here defined is $\|x\| = (x,x)^{1/2} = \left(\sum_{i=1}^{n} |x_i|^2\right)^{1/2}$. Thus the present space is $\mathbf{l}_n^2$ defined in (6c) of Chapter I.

The space $\mathbf{l}^2$ defined in section 8 of Chapter I is also a Hilbert space. The norm $\|x\| = \left(\sum_{i=1}^{\infty} |x_i|^2\right)^{1/2}$ may be derived from an inner product $(x, y) = \sum_{i=1}^{\infty} x_i\overline{y_i}$.

Note that there are convergence difficulties here (not great) which must be met in an orderly fashion.

Similarly, the space $\mathbf{L}^2 = \mathbf{L}^2(\mathcal{E}, \mu)$ introduced in section 8 of Chapter I is a Hilbert space. The inner product is defined by $(f, g) = \int_{\mathcal{E}} f(x) \cdot \overline{g(x)}\, d\mu(x)$.

Now let I be a set of indices having any cardinality. Let $x = (x_\iota)$, $\iota \in \mathrm{I}$, denote a function from I into the scalars which has the value 0 except for at most a denumerable set of values of ι and such that $\sum_{\iota\in \mathrm{I}} |x_\iota|^2 < \infty$. For two such functions x and

$y = (y_\iota)$, write $(x, y) = \sum_{\iota \in I} x_\iota \bar{y}_\iota$. This expression defined on the totality of such functions x gives an inner product (fill in steps). This same totality is then a Hilbert space $\mathbf{H}(\mathrm{I})$. It should be noted that if $\mathrm{I} = \{1, \cdots, n\}$, then $\mathbf{H}(\mathrm{I}) = \mathrm{l}^2_n$. If $\mathrm{I} = \{1, 2, \cdots\}$, then $\mathbf{H}(\mathrm{I}) = \mathrm{l}^2$. We shall see later that every Hilbert space may be considered to be of the type $\mathbf{H}(\mathrm{I})$ for some I. Since the only factor of importance in I is its cardinality, the previous statement amounts to saying that the only invariant of a Hilbert space is its dimension.

2. Linear functionals

We have stated earlier that Hilbert space is characterized by the fact that it is self-adjoint: $\mathbf{H} = \mathbf{H}^*$. In this section we wish to give precise meaning to this statement. We shall have to prove something of the following nature: Every vector g in $\mathbf{H}$ "gives rise" to a linear functional which as a linear functional "behaves like" the element g (isometric isomorphism of $\mathbf{H}$ into $\mathbf{H}^*$); if F is a linear functional over $\mathbf{H}$, then there exists a $g \in \mathbf{H}$ whose "interpretation" as a linear functional is precisely F (the isomorphism is onto). The two statements together show that there exists a mapping (which will obviously be canonical) of $\mathbf{H}$ onto $\mathbf{H}^*$ and which because of its metric and algebraic properties allows us to write $\mathbf{H} = \mathbf{H}^*$.

We commence with the first part of our task. Let $g \in \mathbf{H}$. Consider the mapping $f \to (f, g)$. Let us represent the mapping by F_g and write $F_g f = (f, g)$. We see directly that F_g is a linear functional. Furthermore, since $|F_g f| = |(f, g)| \leq \|f\| \, \|g\|$, we have $\|F_g\| \leq \|g\|$. Also, the fact that $F_g g = \|g\|^2$ proves that $\|F_g\| = \|g\|$. Let us denote the mapping $g \to F_g$ by Ψ. We have thus that Ψ is an isometric map of $\mathbf{H}$ into $\mathbf{H}^*$.

If g_1 and g_2 are two elements in $\mathbf{H}$, it may easily be seen that $F_{g_1+g_2} = F_{g_1} + F_{g_2}$. This comes from the calculation $F_{g_1+g_2} f = (f, g_1 + g_2) = (f, g_1) + (f, g_2) = F_{g_1} f + F_{g_2} f = (F_{g_1} + F_{g_2}) f$. In a similar way we may carry out the calculation $F_{\lambda g}f = (f, \lambda g) = \bar{\lambda}(f, g) = \bar{\lambda}F_g f$. At this point, let us refer to definition 3-1 of Chapter I. We see from equations (10) and (11) that for a linear functional F and for a complex number λ we have two choices in defining λF. Either $(\lambda F)f = \lambda(Ff)$ or $(\lambda F)f = \bar{\lambda}(Ff)$. Clearly, in order to show that Ψ is an isomorphism we must adopt the definition $(\lambda F)f = \bar{\lambda}(Ff)$. From this point of view we see that $F_{\lambda g} = \lambda F_g$. Putting together these results we see that Ψ is an algebraic homomorphism. That is $\Psi(g_1 + g_2) = \Psi g_1 + \Psi g_2$ and $\Psi(\lambda g) = \lambda \Psi g$. Being a homomorphism and an isometry, it is an isomorphism. We may state these results in the form of

THEOREM 2-1: *Let* Ψ *be the mapping from* **H** *into* **H*** *defined by* $\Psi g = F_g$ *where* $F_g f = (f, g)$. *Then* Ψ *is an isometric isomorphism of* **H** *into* **H***.

We now turn to the more substantial task of showing that the isomorphism is onto **H***. This means that if $F \in \mathbf{H}^*$, then there exists $g \in \mathbf{H}$ such that $\Psi g = F$.

It will be sufficient to consider only the case $\|F\| = 1$. Our first task is to find the element g for which we propose the role $\Psi g = F$. The discovery of this element makes full use of the high degree of regularity of Hilbert space.

Since $\|F\| = 1$, there exists a sequence $\{g_n\}$ such that $\|g_n\| = 1$ and $|Fg_n| \to \|F\| = 1$. We may assume (after multiplying by a suitable complex number of modulus 1) that $Fg_n = |Fg_n|$. Thus we have $Fg_n \leq 1$, $Fg_n \to 1$. Let ϵ be chosen so that $0 < \epsilon < 1$; then for sufficiently large n, m, $Fg_n \geq 1 - \epsilon$ and $\|g_n + g_m\| \geq F(g_n + g_m) \geq 2 - 2\epsilon$. By the parallelogram identity (5) we have

$$\text{(6)} \quad \begin{aligned} \|g_n - g_m\|^2 &= 2\|g_n\|^2 + 2\|g_m\|^2 - \|g_n + g_m\|^2 \\ &\leq 4 - (2 - 2\epsilon)^2 < 8\epsilon. \end{aligned}$$

Thus $\{g_n\}$ is a Cauchy sequence. Let us write $g_n \to g$. Then $\|g\| = 1$ $(= \|F\|)$.

We show now that $Ff = (f, g)$ for each $f \in \mathbf{H}$. Holding f fixed, consider first the case in which **H** is a real space. Note that the function $\phi(\lambda) = \|g + \lambda f\|^2$ of the real variable λ is differentiable at $\lambda = 0$ and that $\phi'(0) = 2(f, g)$.[1] This shows, recalling that $\phi(0) = \|g\| = 1$, that the derivative at $\lambda = 0$ of $\|g + \lambda f\|$ is (f, g). Now, for $\lambda > 0$ we have $F(g \pm \lambda f) \leq \|g \pm \lambda f\|$ which along with $Fg = \|g\|$ gives

$$Ff = \lambda^{-1}(F(g + \lambda f) - Fg) \leq \lambda^{-1}(\|g + \lambda f\| - \|g\|)$$

and similarly,

$$Ff = -\lambda^{-1}(F(g - \lambda f) - Fg) \geq -\lambda^{-1}(\|g - \lambda f\| - \|g\|).$$

Referring to the differentiability statement made above, we see (by letting $\lambda \to 0$) that $Ff = (f, g)$.

Suppose now that the space $\mathbf{H}$ is complex. Then exactly as in the proof of the complex form of the Hahn-Banach theorem (theorem 6-2 of Chapter I), we write $Ff = F_1 f - iF_1(if)$ where F_1 is defined to be the real functional (over $\mathbf{H}$ considered as a real space): $F_1 f = \mathcal{R}(Ff)$ where $\mathcal{R}(z)$ means as usual the real part of z. Returning to our above argument we see quickly that $\phi'(0) = \mathcal{R}(f, g)$. Also note that $F_1 g = \|g\|$ and since obviously $\|F_1\| \leq \|F\| = 1$, we have $\|F_1\| = 1$. Thus $F_1(g + \lambda f) \leq \|g + \lambda f\|$. The entire above argument now applies and shows that $F_1 f = \mathcal{R}(f, g)$. Since $F_1(if) = \mathcal{R}(if, g) = -\mathcal{I}(f, g)$ we have $Ff = F_1 f - iF_1(if) = \mathcal{R}(f, g) + i\mathcal{I}(f, g) = (f, g)$. We summarize our results in a theorem (due to Fréchet and F. Riesz).

THEOREM 2-2: *If F is a bounded linear functional over the Hilbert space $\mathbf{H}$, then there exists an element $g \in \mathbf{H}$ such that $Ff = (f, g)$ for all $f \in \mathbf{H}$. In other words, the mapping Ψ of the preceding theorem is onto $\mathbf{H}^*$.*

By virtue of the equality $\mathbf{H} = \mathbf{H}^*$ which we have established, we see that the notion of orthogonality, which for a general Banach space $\mathbf{B}$ is a relation involving subsets of $\mathbf{B}$ and of $\mathbf{B}^*$, is

[1] The computation is simple: $\phi(\lambda) = (g, g) + 2\lambda(f, g) + \lambda^2(f, f)$; hence $\phi'(\lambda) = 2(f, g) + 2\lambda(f, f)$. Finally $\phi'(0) = 2(f, g)$.

for Hilbert spaces meaningful within the context of **H** alone. This fact is of paramount importance to further developments.

3. Orthonormal sets

The elements f and g of **H** are called orthogonal if $(f, g) = 0$. The relation is symmetrical. We sometimes write $f \perp g$. Clearly, if $f \perp g$ then $\lambda f \perp \mu g$ for all scalars λ, μ. An element f is sometimes called *normal* if $\|f\| = 1$. We are now ready to introduce the notion of orthonormal set.

DEFINITION 3-1: *A set of elements* $\{q_\iota\}$, $\iota \in \mathrm{I}$, *is called orthonormal if* $(q_\iota, q_\kappa) = 0$ *for* $\iota \neq \kappa$ *and if* $\|q_\iota\| = 1$, $\iota, \kappa \in \mathrm{I}$.

If q is normal then $\{q\}$ is an orthonormal set.

DEFINITION 3-2: *An orthonormal set* $\{q_\iota\}$, $\iota \in \mathrm{I}$, *is called a complete (or maximal) orthonormal set providing it is not a proper subset of some other orthonormal set.*

Complete orthonormal sets exist. In fact given any orthonormal set, there exists a complete orthonormal set containing the given set as a subset. The proof is derived by a direct application of Zorn's lemma. We obtain below a chain of conditions, each equivalent to the completeness of an orthonormal set.

The following are examples of orthonormal sets in assorted spaces. In each case, they happen to be complete, and this is one of their outstanding properties. In $\mathbf{l}^2_n$, reintroduced in section 1, the vectors $e_1 = (1, 0, \cdots, 0), \cdots, e_n = (0, \cdots 0, 1)$ constitute an orthonormal set of n elements. In $\mathbf{l}^2$ the sequence $e_1 = (1, 0, \cdots), e_2 = (0, 1, 0, \cdots), \cdots$ defines a denumerable orthonormal set. In $\mathbf{L}^2$ with Lebesgue measure on the interval $[0, 1]$, the functions f_n: $f_n(x) = \exp(2\pi i n x)$, $-\infty < n < \infty$, n integral, constitute once more a denumerable orthonormal set.

If $\{q_\iota\}$, $\iota \in \mathrm{I}$, is an orthonormal set and if f is an element in **H**, the numbers $\gamma_\iota = (f, q_\iota)$ are called the *Fourier coefficients* of f with respect to $\{q_\iota\}$. The name reflects the fact that Fourier considered extensively expansions of functions in terms of a particular orthonormal set in $\mathbf{L}^2$. We derive below for abstract Hilbert spaces a host of results originally obtained in the field of Fourier series—these carry the names of Bessel, Fourier, and Parseval.

First, let us establish the Bessel inequality.

THEOREM 3-1: *Let* $\{q_1, \cdots, q_n\}$ *be a finite orthonormal set and let* $f \in \mathbf{H}$. *Let* $\gamma_i = (f, q_i)$, $i = 1, \cdots, n$. *Then*

$$\|f\|^2 \geq \sum_{i=1}^{n} |\gamma_i|^2. \tag{7}$$

Proof: We have

$$\begin{aligned} 0 &\leq \left\| f - \sum_{i=1}^{n} \gamma_i q_i \right\|^2 \\ &= \|f\|^2 - \sum_{i=1}^{n} (f, \gamma_i q_i) - \sum_{i=1}^{n} (\gamma_i q_i, f) + \sum_{i,j=1}^{n} (\gamma_i q_i, \gamma_j q_j) \\ &= \|f\|^2 - \sum_{i=1}^{n} |\gamma_i|^2. \end{aligned}$$

At the last step we have made use of the fact $(q_i, q_j) = 0$ if $i \neq j$. The theorem yields quickly the following result.

THEOREM 3-2: *Let* $\{q_\iota\}$, $\iota \in \mathrm{I}$, *be an orthonormal set and let* $f \in \mathbf{H}$. *If* $\gamma_\iota = (f, q_\iota)$, *then* $\gamma_\iota = 0$, *excepting at most denumerably many indices.*

Proof: Let $\epsilon > 0$ and let n be any integer satisfying $n > \|f\|^2/\epsilon$. Then by the preceding result the number of indices ι for which $|\gamma_\iota|^2 > \epsilon$ is less than n. This leads to the conclusion.

By virtue of the preceding two results we see that for any orthonormal set $\sum_{\iota \in \mathrm{I}} |\gamma_\iota|^2 \leq \|f\|^2$. In fact, the expression $\sum_{\iota \in \mathrm{I}} |\gamma_\iota|^2$

contains at most denumerably many non-zero terms. The general inequality is then obtained by going from the finite case (7) and then passing to the limit.

THEOREM 3-3: *Let* $\{q_\iota\}$, $\iota \in I$, *be an orthonormal set and let* $f \in \mathbf{H}$. *Let* $\gamma_\iota = (f, q_\iota)$. *Then the* series $\sum_{\iota \in I} \gamma_\iota q_\iota$ *converges strongly to an element* f'. *Furthermore* $f - f' \perp q_\iota$ *for each* $\iota \in I$.

Since $\gamma_\iota = 0$ excepting at most denumerably many indices ι, we may assume that we are dealing with a finite or denumerable orthonormal set which we shall denote by $\{q_n\}$, $n = 1, \cdots, N$ or $n = 1, \cdots$. If the set $\{q_n\}$ is finite the result is obvious, so, let us assume it to be infinite. Write $f_r = \sum_{i=1}^{r} \gamma_i q_i$. Then for $s > r$ we have $\|f_s - f_r\|^2 = \sum_{i=r+1}^{s} |\gamma_i|^2$ and since $\sum_{i=1}^{\infty} |\gamma_i|^2 \leq \|f\|^2$, we see that $\{f_r\}$ is a Cauchy sequence. Let it converge to f'. Note that $(f', q_n) = \gamma_n$, since $(f_r, q_n) = \gamma_n$ for $r \geq n$ and since $f_r \to f'$. Thus $f - f' \perp q_n$, which terminates the proof. Note that the convergence of $\sum_{i=1}^{\infty} \gamma_i q_i$ to f' is independent of the order of summation.

THEOREM 3-4: *Let* $\{q_\iota\}$, $\iota \in I$, *be an orthonormal set and let* $\mathbf{M}$ *be the smallest closed linear manifold containing the elements* q_ι, $\iota \in I$. *Then either* $\mathbf{M} = \mathbf{H}$ *or there exists an element* q *with* $\|q\| = 1$ *orthogonal to each* $q_\iota : (q, q_\iota) = 0$, $\iota \in I$.

Suppose $\mathbf{M} \neq \mathbf{H}$. Then there exists a linear functional $F \neq 0$ such that $F \perp \mathbf{M}$ (by theorem 6-5 of Chapter I). We may assume that $\|F\| = 1$. Furthermore, by theorem 2-2, $Ff = (f, q)$ for some $q \in \mathbf{H}$ and with $\|q\| = 1$. Thus $(q_\iota, q) = 0$ since $q \perp \mathbf{M}$.

Note that if $\mathbf{M} \neq \mathbf{H}$, the set $\{q_\iota\}$ is not complete since by adjoining q to it, we enlarge it.

We are now ready to state a theorem which reveals the many-sided importance of the notion of complete orthonormal set

THEOREM 3-5: *Let* $\{q_\iota\}$, $\iota \in \mathrm{I}$, *be an orthonormal set. The following statements are equivalent:*

(a) *The set* $\{q_\iota\}$ *is complete.*

(b) *If for* $f \in \mathbf{H}$, $(f, q_\iota) = 0$ *for each* ι, *then* $f = 0$.

(c) *The smallest closed linear manifold containing each* q_ι *is* $\mathbf{H}$.

(d) *For every* $f \in \mathbf{H}$, $f = \sum_{\iota \in \mathrm{I}} \gamma_\iota q_\iota$, *where* $\gamma_\iota = (f, q_\iota)$ (*Fourier expansion*).

(e) *For every* $f, g \in \mathbf{H}$, $(f, g) = \sum_{\iota \in \mathrm{I}} \gamma_\iota \bar{\delta}_\iota$ *where* γ_ι *is as above and* $\delta_\iota = (g, q_\iota)$ (*Parseval identity*).

(f) *For every* $f \in \mathbf{H}$, $\|f\|^2 = \sum_{\iota \in \mathrm{I}} |\gamma_\iota|^2$.

We prove the following implications:

(a) $\Rightarrow$ (b) $\Rightarrow$ (c) $\Rightarrow$ (d) $\Rightarrow$ (e) $\Rightarrow$ (f) $\Rightarrow$ (a).

(a) $\Rightarrow$ (b). If $(f, q_\iota) = 0$ for each ι, either $f = 0$ or we may assume that $\|f\| = 1$. In the latter case, we can enlarge the orthonormal set $\{q_\iota\}$ by adjoining f to it.

(b) $\Rightarrow$ (c). This is proved in theorem 3-4.

(c) $\Rightarrow$ (d). According to theorem 3-3, write $f' = \sum_{\iota \in \mathrm{I}} \gamma_\iota q_\iota$. Then $f - f' \perp q_\iota$ for each ι and hence $f - f'$ is orthogonal to the closed linear manifold generated by the q_ι. This manifold is $\mathbf{H}$ by hypothesis. Thus $(f - f', f - f') = 0$ and $f = f'$.

(d) $\Rightarrow$ (e). The result: $(f, g) = \sum_{\iota \in \mathrm{I}} \gamma_\iota \bar{\delta}_\iota$ is trivial if the summation contains a finite number of non-zero terms. In the general case, one applies a limiting argument using the fact that (f, g) is a continuous function of its arguments.

(e) $\Rightarrow$ (f). Calculate (f, f) according to (e).

(f) $\Rightarrow$ (a). If $\{q_\iota\}$ is not complete, there exists a vector q with $\|q\| = 1$, $(q_\iota, q) = 0$. By (f), $\|q\|^2 = \sum_{\iota \in \mathrm{I}} |(q, q_\iota)|^2 = 0$. This contradiction shows that $\{q_\iota\}$ is complete.

4. Unbounded transformations and their adjoints

If T is a bounded linear transformation from $\mathbf{B}$ into $\mathbf{C}$, its adjoint T^* has already been defined and transforms $\mathbf{C}^*$ into $\mathbf{B}^*$. The defining equation is $(T^*F)f = F(Tf)$, $f \in \mathbf{B}$, $F \in \mathbf{C}^*$. If for $\mathbf{B}$ and $\mathbf{C}$ we choose the same Hilbert space $\mathbf{H}$, we have $\mathbf{B} = \mathbf{B}^* = \mathbf{C} = \mathbf{C}^*$ and may therefore define the adjoint by

$$(Tf, g) = (f, T^*g) \tag{8}$$

for all $f, g \in \mathbf{H}$.

We wish now to consider transformations T more general than the bounded ones defined over the entire space $\mathbf{H}$. We shall assume that the domain of definition of T is a subset Δ (or Δ_T) of $\mathbf{H}$. We shall assume that Δ is linear (it contains $\alpha f + \beta g$ whenever it contains f and g). We shall also make the important assumption that Δ is dense in $\mathbf{H}$.

Given such a transformation T, consider the pairs $\{g, h\}$ such that

$$(Tf, g) = (f, h) \tag{9}$$

for all $f \in \Delta$. The totality of these pairs has certain properties which we now investigate.

In the first place, if $\{g, h\}$ and $\{g, h'\}$ are two such pairs, then $h = h'$. This arises from the fact that in accordance with (9), $(f, h) = (f, h')$ for f belonging to a set Δ dense in $\mathbf{H}$. Thus $h - h' \perp \mathbf{H}$ and $h - h' = 0$. Next, if $\{g_1, h_1\}$ and $\{g_2, h_2\}$ are admissible pairs, so is $\{\alpha_1 g_1 + \alpha_2 g_2, \alpha_1 h_1 + \alpha_2 h_2\}$ for all α_1 and α_2. Finally, suppose $\{g_n, h_n\}$ is an admissible pair, $n = 1, 2, \cdots$. Suppose further that $g_n \to g$ and $h_n \to h$. Then $\{g, h\}$ is admissible. This can be checked directly from the facts that $(Tf, g_n) = (f, h_n)$ and that $(Tf, g_n) \to (Tf, g)$, $(f, h_n) \to (f, h)$.

Now, let Δ_* represent the set of all first elements g in the admissible pairs $\{g, h\}$. We see that Δ_* is a linear manifold in $\mathbf{H}$. It need not be dense in $\mathbf{H}$. Let T^* be the transformation defined on Δ_* by $T^*g = h$. We see that T^* is well defined (we are referring to the $h = h'$ argument), that T^* is linear, and finally, that T^* is a closed transformation in the sense of the definition 4-1 of Chapter II. We may write, furthermore,

$$(Tf, g) = (f, T^*g) \tag{10}$$

for $f \in \Delta$ and $g \in \Delta_*$.

DEFINITION 4-1: *The transformation T^* defined above is called the adjoint of the transformation T.*

Note that if T is bounded (and defined over **H**), the present definition yields the same transformation T^* as the earlier definition of Chapter II. Note also that T^* is a closed transformation.

We now introduce a most important type of transformation.

DEFINITION 4-2: *Let A be a linear transformation defined over a domain Δ which is dense in* **H**. *Let A^* be the adjoint of A and let the domain of definition of A^* be Δ_*.*
We shall say that A is self-adjoint providing that

(a) $\Delta = \Delta_*$;

(b) $Af = A^*f$ *on* Δ.

A transformation A is called *symmetric* providing $(Af, g) = (f, Ag)$ for all $f, g \in \Delta$. Thus all self-adjoint transformations are *symmetric*. An interesting phenomenon which may present itself for a given A is that $\Delta \subset \Delta_*$, $\Delta \neq \Delta_*$, and that $A = A^*$ on Δ. Such transformations are not self-adjoint (see section 8 for an example).

We now state a theorem which at the time of its discovery by Hellinger and Toeplitz one-half century ago aroused both admiration and puzzlement. The reason for the perplexity lies in the fact that it mixes two phenomena, the closure of the adjoint transformation and the fact that a closed everywhere-defined transformation is bounded (theorem 4-2 of Chapter II).

THEOREM 4-1: *Let A be a self-adjoint transformation whose domain of definition Δ is all of* **H**. *Then A is bounded.*

We shall be concerned later with the determination of the structure of an arbitrary *self-adjoint* transformation. To that end we shall prove now a theorem of the greatest value in our later work. In terms of language to be introduced later, the theorem states that the spectrum of a self-adjoint transformation is real.

THEOREM 4-2: *Let A be a self-adjoint transformation with domain Δ and let $c = \lambda + i\mu$ be a complex number with $\mu \neq 0$. Then the transformation $(cI - A)$ maps Δ onto* **H** *in a one-to-one manner. The transformation $(cI - A)^{-1}$ is bounded and*

$$\|(cI - A)^{-1}\| \leq |\mu|^{-1}.$$

Proof: For $g \in \Delta$, let $f = (cI - A)g$. Consider the quantity $(f, f) = ((cI - A)g, (cI - A)g)$. For $cI - A$, write $(\lambda I - A) + i\mu I$. Upon expanding the above inner product we obtain four terms. The middle terms $((\lambda I - A)g, i\mu g)$ and $(i\mu g, (\lambda I - A)g)$ cancel each other because $A^* = A$.[2] Thus we have the very important equality:

$$\|f\|^2 = \|(\lambda I - A)g\|^2 + \mu^2\|g\|^2. \tag{11}$$

Note that all quantities here are non-negative. In particular, $g \neq 0$ implies $f \neq 0$. Thus the transformation $(cI - A)$ is bijective from Δ to its range, and on its range the inverse transformation $(cI - A)^{-1}$ is defined. Also, $(cI - A)^{-1}f = g$ and since $\|g\|^2 \leq \mu^{-2}\|f\|^2$, we see that $\|(cI - A)^{-1}f\| \leq |\mu|^{-1}\|f\|$. This gives the estimate for the bound of $(cI - A)^{-1}$.

To complete the proof, we must show that the range of $cI - A$ is **H**. We do this in two stages. First we show that the range (which is a linear manifold) is dense in **H**. Next we show that it is **H**. Toward the first part, suppose h is orthogonal to all elements $(cI - A)g$, $g \in \Delta$. Then $((cI - A)g, h) = 0$ or $(Ag, h) =$

[2] The computation follows: $((\lambda I - A)g, i\mu g) = (\lambda g, i\mu g) - (Ag, i\mu g) = -(i\mu g, \lambda g) + (i\mu g, Ag) = -(i\mu g, (\lambda I - A)g)$.

$(g, \bar{c}h)$ for all $g \in \Delta$. This implies that h is in the domain of A^* and that $A^*h = \bar{c}h$. Since A is self-adjoint, we have $Ah = \bar{c}h$. Hence $\bar{c}(h, h) = (\bar{c}h, h) = (Ah, h) = (h, Ah) = (h, \bar{c}h) = c(h, h)$ and since $c \neq \bar{c}$, $h = 0$. This shows that the range of $(cI - A)$ is dense in $\mathbf{H}$.

We show now that the range is all of $\mathbf{H}$. Let f be arbitrary in $\mathbf{H}$ and let $\{f_n\}$ be a sequence of elements which belong to the range and such that $f_n \to f$. Let g_n be the solution of the equation $(cI - A)g_n = f_n$. Then we have: $\|f_n - f_m\|^2 = \|(\lambda I - A)(g_n - g_m)\|^2 + \mu^2\|g_n - g_m\|^2 \geq \mu^2\|g_n - g_m\|^2$. Thus the sequence $\{g_n\}$ is a Cauchy sequence. Suppose $g_n \to g$. Since A is a closed transformation, it follows that g belongs to the domain of A and that $(cI - A)g = f$. This shows that the range of $(cI - A)$ is all of $\mathbf{H}$.

5. Projections

Projections in a Banach space have already been defined to be idempotent bounded linear transformations. In Hilbert space we require of a projection P the additional property that it be self-adjoint, $P^* = P$.

DEFINITION 5-1: *A projection P in Hilbert space is a bounded linear transformation which satisfies $P^2 = P$, $P^* = P$.*

Let P be a projection and let $\{\mathbf{M}, \mathbf{N}\}$ be the complementary pair of linear manifolds associated with P. (Thus $Pf = f$ for $f \in \mathbf{M}$, $Pf = 0$ for $f \in \mathbf{N}$.) Suppose $g \in \mathbf{M}$ and $h \in \mathbf{N}$. Then $(g, h) = (Pg, h) = (g, P^*h) = (g, Ph) = (g, 0) = 0$. This shows that $\mathbf{N} \subset \mathbf{M}^\perp$. Next, let $h \in \mathbf{M}^\perp$ and let f be arbitrary. Then $(f, Ph) = (f, P^*h) = (Pf, h) = 0$. Thus $Ph = 0$ and $h \in \mathbf{N}$, and thus $\mathbf{M}^\perp \subset \mathbf{N}$. We see therefore that $\mathbf{N} = \mathbf{M}^\perp$. In Hilbert space, a projection is completely defined by one closed linear manifold. For that reason one says that P is the *orthogonal projection* on $\mathbf{M}$.

If $f \in \mathbf{H}$, then Pf is orthogonal to $f - Pf$ and $\|f\|^2 = \|Pf\|^2 + \|f - Pf\|^2$. This implies that $\|P\| \leq 1$. Since for any projection $\neq O$ we have $\|P\| \geq 1$, we have $\|P\| = 1$ unless $P = O$.

In section 6 of Chapter II we introduced the notation $P_1 \succ P_2$ to indicate that $\mathbf{M}_1 \supset \mathbf{M}_2$ and $\mathbf{N}_1 \subset \mathbf{N}_2$ where the manifolds have the obvious meaning. In Hilbert space we need require only that $\mathbf{M}_1 \supset \mathbf{M}_2$ since this implies that $\mathbf{N}_1 \subset \mathbf{N}_2$.

THEOREM 5-1: *Let $\{P_n\}$ be an increasing sequence of projections in Hilbert space, $P_1 \prec P_2 \prec \cdots$, and let f be arbitrary in* $\mathbf{H}$. *Then the sequence $\{P_n f\}$ converges strongly to an element Pf. The mapping $P: f \rightarrow Pf$ is a projection. In fact, P is the orthogonal projection on the smallest closed linear manifold* $\mathbf{M}$ *which contains each manifold $\mathbf{M}_n$, where P_n is the orthogonal projection on $\mathbf{M}_n$.*

We show first that $\{P_n f\}$ is a Cauchy sequence. We have from the hypothesis $P_1 \prec P_2 \prec \cdots$ that $\|P_1 f\|^2 + \|(P_2 - P_1)f\|^2 + \cdots + \|(P_n - P_{n-1})f\|^2 = \|P_n f\|^2 \leq \|f\|^2$.[3] Hence the series $\sum_{n=1}^{\infty} \|(P_{n+1} - P_n)f\|^2$ converges. Let $n > m$. Then $\|P_n f - P_m f\|^2 = \|(P_n - P_{n-1})f\|^2 + \cdots + \|(P_{m+1} - P_m)f\|^2$. This argument shows that $\{P_n f\}$ converges. Let us write $P_n f \rightarrow Pf$.

It is clear that P is linear and bounded, $\|P\| \leq 1$. Also, for any n, $PP_n f = P_n f$. Letting $n \rightarrow \infty$, this gives $PP = P$. We see also that $P_n P f = P_n f$. Hence $P_n P = PP_n$. We have, obviously, that $P^* = P$ and hence P is a projection. That P is an orthogonal projection on a manifold which includes each $\mathbf{M}_n$ (defined in the theorem) is obvious since $f \in \mathbf{M}_n$ implies $Pf = f$. If f is orthogonal to each $\mathbf{M}_n$, $Pf = O$. This completes the proof.

It should be noted that $P \succ P_n$ for each n. Also if $Q \succ P_n$ for each n, then $Q \succ P$. Thus P is the supremum of $\{P_n\}$.

[3] First of all if $r < s$, then $((P_s - P_{s-1})f, (P_r - P_{r-1})f) = ((P_r - P_{r-1})(P_s - P_{s-1})f, f) = ((P_r - P_{r-1} - P_r + P_{r-1})f, f) = 0$ because $P_r P_s = P_r$, etc. Hence $\|P_n f\|^2 = \|[(P_n - P_{n-1}) + \cdots + (P_2 - P_1) + P_1]f\|^2 = \|(P_n - P_{n-1})f\|^2 + \cdots + \|(P_2 - P_1)f\|^2 + \|P_1 f\|^2$ since all cross terms in the inner-product expansion cancel.

6. Resolutions of the identity

We introduce now a concept which is very important in the study of self-adjoint transformations, that of resolution of the identity. The fundamental theorem will be to the effect that every self-adjoint transformation has associated to it a resolution of the identity (essentially unique) with the help of which the self-adjoint transformation may be reconstructed in a manner which is essentially simple. We shall proceed by first defining the notion of resolution of the identity and then showing how to associate a self-adjoint transformation to such a resolution. The inverse problem of obtaining the resolution from the transformation is much more difficult and will be considered in the next chapter. Let us set down forthwith

DEFINITION 6-1: *A family of projections* E_λ, $-\infty < \lambda < \infty$, *is called a resolution of the identity if and only if*

(12a) $\lambda < \mu$ *implies* $E_\lambda \prec E_\mu$;

(12b) $\lambda_n \to -\infty$ *implies* $E_{\lambda_n} \to O$ *strongly;*
$\lambda_n \to \infty$ *implies* $E_{\lambda_n} \to I$ *strongly;*

(12c) *whenever* $\{\lambda_n\}$ *is an increasing sequence such that* $\lambda_n \to \lambda$, *then* $E_{\lambda_n} \to E_\lambda$ *strongly.*

Some remarks. We remind the reader that $A_n \to A$ strongly means $A_n f \to Af$ for every f. Next, by virtue of condition (12c) we see that the family E_λ is continuous on the left. Thus the concept we have defined should more properly be called a *left resolution of the identity*. We may have similarly right resolutions of the identity or resolutions which are neither left nor right [if we omit condition (12c) of the definition].

If we take a family of projections E_λ satisfying (12a) and (12b), it is easy to construct from it a (left) resolution of the identity which satisfies also (12c). The procedure is similar to that used for replacing a monotone function by one continuous from the left. Let λ be fixed and let $\{\lambda_n\}$ be an increasing sequence for which $\lambda_n \to \lambda$. Then by theorem 5-1, E_{λ_n} converges to a projection E'_λ for which $E'_\lambda < E_\lambda$. It is easy to see that the family E'_λ is a resolution of the identity.

Let us denote by $E_{\lambda+0}$ the projection which is the limit of any sequence $E_{\lambda+\epsilon_n}$ where $\epsilon_n > 0$ and $\epsilon_n \to 0$ is a monotone fashion. If we define $E_{\lambda-0}$ in a similar fashion we see that $E_{\lambda-0} = E_\lambda$ by condition (12c). If $E_{\lambda+0} \neq E_\lambda$, we say that the resolution has a discontinuity or *jump* at the value λ. If $E_{\lambda+0} = E_\lambda$, the resolution is continuous at λ. If for some $\epsilon > 0$, $E_{\lambda-\epsilon} = E_{\lambda+\epsilon}$, then the resolution is constant in a neighborhood of λ. The reader should convince himself that in a finite-dimensional space, a resolution of the identity is constant for all λ except for a finite set $\lambda_1, \cdots, \lambda_n$ at which a jump occurs. In a separable infinite-dimensional Hilbert space (one of denumerably infinite dimensionality) the number of jumps is at most denumerable. In such spaces there are resolutions which are continuous at each λ and constant at no λ. The reader is advised to construct as many different types of resolutions as possible.

A final remark. It may be that for some λ_0, $E_{\lambda_0} = O$. In that case, $E_\lambda = O$ for $\lambda < \lambda_0$. We say that the resolution is *bounded from below*. In that case there exists a maximum number l such that $E_l = O$ and $E_{l+\epsilon} \neq O$ for $\epsilon > 0$. The number l is called the *lower bound of the resolution*. Similarly, if there exists a λ_0 such that $E_{\lambda_0} = I$, we say that the resolution is *bounded from above*. There exists then a unique number u such that for all $\epsilon > 0$, $E_{u+\epsilon} = I$ and $E_{u-\epsilon} \neq I$. We shall call u the *upper bound of the resolution;* clearly, $E_{u+0} = I$. Throughout the remainder of this chapter we shall be interested exclusively in bounded (on both sides) resolutions of the identity.

We proceed now to develop a theory of integration of the Stieltjes type which associates to every resolution of the identity E_λ a self-adjoint transformation A. We shall write the integral in the form

$$A = \int \lambda \, dE_\lambda, \tag{13}$$

it being understood that the limits of integration are l and $u + 0$.

To this effect let n be a positive integer and let $\lambda_0, \cdots, \lambda_n$ be chosen so that $\lambda_0 < \lambda_1 < \cdots < \lambda_n$, and that $\lambda_0 < l$, $\lambda_n > u$. Write E_i for $E_{\lambda_i} - E_{\lambda_{i-1}}$. Since $E_{\lambda_i} > E_{\lambda_{i-1}}$, we see that E_i is a projection and hence that $E_iE_i = E_i$. Also, it is easy to check that if $i \neq j$, $E_iE_j = 0$. For suppose that $i > j$ and hence $\lambda_i > \lambda_j$. Remembering that we have for any r and s, $E_{\lambda_r}E_{\lambda_s} = E_{\lambda_s}E_{\lambda_r} = E_{\lambda_t}$ where t is the minimum of r and s, we have $E_iE_j = (E_{\lambda_i} - E_{\lambda_{i-1}})(E_{\lambda_j} - E_{\lambda_{j-1}}) = E_{\lambda_i}E_{\lambda_j} - E_{\lambda_{i-1}}E_{\lambda_j} - E_{\lambda_i}E_{\lambda_{j-1}} + E_{\lambda_{i-1}}E_{\lambda_{j-1}} = E_{\lambda_j} - E_{\lambda_j} - E_{\lambda_{j-1}} + E_{\lambda_{j-1}} = O$.

We have also $\sum_{i=1}^{n} E_i = I$ since $E_{\lambda_0} = O$ and $E_{\lambda_n} = I$. Therefore for $f \in \mathbf{H}$, we have $\|f\|^2 = (f, f) = \left(\sum_{i=1}^{n} E_if, \sum_{j=1}^{n} E_jf\right) = \sum_{i,j=1}^{n} (E_if, E_jf) = \sum_{i=1}^{n} (E_if, E_if) = \sum_{i=1}^{n} \|E_if\|^2$.

Now let λ_i' be chosen to satisfy $\lambda_{i-1} \leq \lambda_i' \leq \lambda_i$. Let us consider the sum $\sum_{i=1}^{n} \lambda_i'E_i$. Since the E_i are self-adjoint and the λ_i' are real, the sum is a self-adjoint operator. The integral in (13) will be defined in such a way as to be a limit of sums $\sum_{i=1}^{n} \lambda_i'E_i$, the limit being taken in the uniform topology of operators. Since a limit of self-adjoint operators is self-adjoint, A will also be self-adjoint. Another fact here is worth noting. If B is a transformation which commutes with E_λ for each value of λ, then B commutes with $\sum_{i=1}^{n} \lambda_i'E_i$. Thus finally B commutes with the limit of sums of this type, namely, A.

Let us now consider the question of the convergence of the integral. We shall prove the following: Let $\epsilon > 0$ and let the numbers λ_i, $i = 0, \cdots, n$ mentioned above be so chosen that $\lambda_i - \lambda_{i-1} < \epsilon$. Now choose an integer m and numbers μ_0, μ_1,

$\cdots, \mu_m$ such that $\mu_0 < l$, $\mu_m > u$, $\mu_0 < \mu_1 < \cdots < \mu_m$, and $\mu_i - \mu_{i-1} < \epsilon$. Choose also μ_i' so that $\mu_{i-1} \leq \mu_i' \leq \mu_i$. Let us write $S_\lambda = \sum_{i=1}^{n} \lambda_i' E_i$ and $S_\mu = \sum_{i=1}^{m} \mu_i'(E_{\mu_i} - E_{\mu_{i-1}})$. We assert then that $\|S_\lambda - S_\mu\| \leq 2\epsilon$. This fact will serve as a basis for the definition of the integral which we make at this point—as the limit of sums S_λ formed for a sequence of gratings of the type $\lambda_0, \cdots, \lambda_n$ for which the maximum value of $\lambda_i - \lambda_{i-1}$ approaches zero.

Consider the union of the set $\lambda_0, \cdots, \lambda_n$ and $\mu_0, \cdots, \mu_m$. Let the members of this union be the points $\nu_0, \nu_1, \cdots, \nu_r$ where $\nu_0 < \nu_1 < \cdots < \nu_r$. Then we may write

$$S_\lambda - S_\mu = \sum_{i=1}^{r} \rho_i(E_{\nu_i} - E_{\nu_{i-1}})$$

where each ρ_i is the difference of some λ_j' and μ_k'. It is also clear that for each i, $|\rho_i| \leq 2\epsilon$. Thus, by a computation similar to one made earlier, we have

$$\begin{aligned} \|(S_\lambda - S_\mu)f\|^2 &= \sum_{i=1}^{r} \rho_i^2 \|(E_{\nu_i} - E_{\nu_{i-1}})f\|^2 \\ &\leq 4\epsilon^2 \sum_{i=1}^{r} \|(E_{\nu_i} - E_{\nu_{i-1}})f\|^2 \\ &= 4\epsilon^2 \|f\|^2, \end{aligned}$$

which implies that $\|S_\lambda - S_\mu\| \leq 2\epsilon$.

Some final observations. It is quite clear that we may choose λ_0 and λ_n so that $\lambda_0 < l < \lambda_1$ and $\lambda_{n-1} < u < \lambda_n$ and hence that the norm of the transformation S_λ satisfies $\|S_\lambda\| \leq \max(|l| + \epsilon, |u| + \epsilon)$. This shows that $\|A\| \leq \max(|l|, |u|)$. Suppose that we introduce

DEFINITION 6-2: *If A and B are bounded self-adjoint transformations, we shall write $A \geq B$ if and only if for all f, $(Af, f) \geq (Bf, f)$.*

We note quickly that $(l - \epsilon)I < \lambda_0 I \leq S_\lambda \leq \lambda_n I < (u + \epsilon)I$. Hence, remembering that S_λ converges to A uniformly and that $\epsilon > 0$ is arbitrary, we have by taking limits $lI \leq A \leq uI$.

A suggested exercise: Prove that if A and B in definition 6-2 are projections, then $A \geq B$ if and only if $A \succ B$.

We sum up all these results in

THEOREM 6-1: *Let E_λ be a bounded resolution of the identity with lower and upper bounds l and u respectively. The integral*

$$A = \int \lambda \, dE_\lambda$$

as defined above exists, the convergence being in the sense of the uniform topology of operators. The transformation A is self-adjoint and it commutes with all operators B which commute with E_λ for each value of λ. It satisfies $\|A\| \leq \max(|l|, |u|)$ and $lI \leq A \leq uI$.

Let us review once more the problem before us and the extent of our achievement. We have seen how, given a resolution of the identity, we can associate with it by a simple procedure embodied in formula (13) a self-adjoint transformation.[4] So far, we have considered only bounded resolutions. The procedure can be extended to unbounded resolutions and yields once more a self-adjoint transformation, this time unbounded. This extension requires care but it is not mysterious; we could, if we wished, carry it out at this point. The converse problem is of a completely different order of difficulty: Given a self-adjoint A, to find the resolution of the identity E_λ associated with it such that A is related to E_λ by formula (13). In case A is bounded the solution was given by Hilbert in about 1906. The unbounded case presents entirely new types of difficulties and was resolved much later.[5] We shall solve this problem (both cases simultaneously)

[4] We urge the reader to consider integrals of the form $\int \phi(\lambda) \, dE_\lambda$ where ϕ is a function which is continuous (consider it to be real and defined over the interval $[l - \epsilon, u + \epsilon]$). The value of the integral is denoted by $\phi(A)$. Expressions of this sort will be met later.

[5] By von Neumann, Stone, F. Riesz, and others.

in the fifth chapter using as our basic idea a result begotten by theorem 4-2.

7. Unitary transformations

The unitary transformations in Hilbert space correspond to the more familiar rotations about the origin in simpler spaces. We shall first introduce a theorem and then discuss the immediately obvious properties of these transformations.

THEOREM 7-1: *For a bounded linear transformation U, the following conditions are equivalent:*

(a) $UU^* = U^*U = I$;

(b) U^{-1} *exists and* $(f, g) = (Uf, Ug)$ *for all* f, g *in* $\mathbf{H}$;

(c) U^{-1} *exists and* $\|f\| = \|Uf\|$ *for all* f *in* $\mathbf{H}$.

Proof: (a) $\Rightarrow$ (b). From (a) it is clear that U^{-1} exists and is equal to U^*. Also $(f, g) = (f, U^*Ug) = (Uf, Ug)$ for all f and g. Next, (b) $\Rightarrow$ (c) as can be seen by writing f for g in (b).

We show that (c) $\Rightarrow$ (b). From (c) we have $(f + g, f + g) = (U(f + g), U(f + g))$. If $\mathbf{H}$ is a real space, a simple expansion of this equation gives $(f, g) = (Uf, Ug)$. If $\mathbf{H}$ is complex we have equality of the real parts. A similar operation on $\|f + ig\|^2 = \|U(f + ig)\|^2$ gives the equality of the imaginary parts. Hence (c) implies (b). Now (b) implies that $(f, g) = (U^*Uf, g)$ for all f, g in $\mathbf{H}$ and hence that $U^*U = I$. Since in addition U^{-1} exists, it is clear that $U^{-1} = U^*$ and this gives (a).

DEFINITION 7-1: *A transformation U satisfying any of the conditions* (a), (b), (c) *of the preceding theorem is called unitary.*

It is clear that I is unitary, that U^{-1} is unitary if U is unitary, and that $U \cdot V$ is unitary if U and V are ($(UV)(UV)^* = UVV^*U^* = I$, etc.). Thus the unitary transformations constitute a group, the *unitary group*. It is clearly one of the most important groups of operators. Its presence raises immediately the question of *unitary equivalence* of two operators A and B: *Does there exist a unitary U such that $B = U^*AU$?* This question is of particular prominence in case A and B are self-adjoint. The answers (a complete set of unitary invariants) are known.

The condition $(f, g) = (Uf, Ug)$ implies that $U^*U = I$ and hence that U has a left inverse. For finite-dimensional spaces, any left inverse is also a right inverse. For infinite-dimensional spaces this need not be so.

It is clear that the transformation λI is self-adjoint if and only if λ is a real number. Similarly, it is obvious that αI is unitary if and only if $|\alpha| = 1$, that is, $\alpha = \exp(i\lambda)$ where $0 < \lambda \leq 2\pi$. We are now in a position to describe the key structure theorem for unitary transformations, which theorem is very close in spirit to that for self-adjoint transformations. Let us begin with the part which is within reach.

THEOREM 7-2: *Let E_λ be a bounded resolution of the identity for which $E_0 = O$ and $E_{2\pi+0} = I$. Then the integral*

$$U = \int_0^{2\pi} \exp(i\lambda)\, dE_\lambda \tag{14}$$

exists in the uniform topology and represents a unitary transformation.

The proof of this parallels step by step that given earlier. We utilize here sums of the form $\sum_{j=1}^{n} \exp(i\lambda_j')E_j$ instead of $\sum_{j=1}^{n} \lambda_j' E_j$. We leave all further elaboration to the reader.

The converse theorem (which we shall not prove here) is that every unitary U has associated with it a unique resolution of the identity E_λ satisfying (14). This result was first established by von Neumann in 1929.

8. Examples and exercises

Let $\tau(x, y)$ be a function defined on the unit square $0 \leq x \leq 1$ and $0 \leq y \leq 1$. Suppose at first that τ is continuous in the square. It is therefore bounded and we have, say, $|\tau(x, y)| \leq \mathrm{k}$ for all such x, y. Let $f \in \mathbf{C}_{[0,1]}$ and set $g(x) = \int_0^1 \tau(x, y)f(y)\,dy$. It is clear that g is continuous, that is, $g \in \mathbf{C}_{[0,1]}$ and that the mapping $f \to g = Tf$ is linear. It is also bounded as may be seen from the fact that $|g(x)| \leq \int_0^1 |\tau(x, y)|\,|f(y)|\,dy \leq \mathrm{k} \cdot \|f\| \int_0^1 dy = \mathrm{k}\|f\|$. Thus $\|g\| \leq \mathrm{k}\|f\|$. This example illustrates the easiest type of situation one meets in the theory of integral operators in $\mathbf{C}_{[0,1]}$.

Let us now cast a glance at an integral operator in Hilbert space. Let $\tau(x, y)$ be a function which is Lebesgue measurable and with $|\tau(x, y)|$ square integrable in the unit square $0 \leq x \leq 1$, $0 \leq y \leq 1$. Then the theory of integration allows us to write down the equations: $\int_0^1 \int_0^1 |\tau(x, y)|^2\,dS = \int_0^1 dx \int_0^1 |\tau(x, y)|^2\,dy = \int_0^1 \|\tau(x, \cdot)\|^2\,dx = \mathrm{k}^2$ (say), where $\|\tau(x, \cdot)\| \geq 0$ is square integrable—we shall write: $\|\tau(x, \cdot)\| \in \mathbf{L}^2_{[0.1]}$. Let $f \in \mathbf{L}^2_{[0.1]}$ and set $g(x) = \int_0^1 \tau(x, y)f(y)\,dy$. Then it may be seen that $g \in \mathbf{L}^2_{[0.1]}$. Indeed, we have $\int_0^1 |g(x)|^2\,dx = \int_0^1 \left| \int_0^1 \tau(x, y)f(y)\,dy \right|^2 dx \leq \int_0^1 \left[\int_0^1 |\tau(x, y)|^2\,dy \cdot \int_0^1 |f(y)|^2\,dy\right] dx = \int_0^1 \|\tau(x, \cdot)\|^2\|f\|^2\,dx \leq \mathrm{k}^2\|f\|^2$, where the critical step is obtained with the Schwarz inequality. This states that $\|g\| \leq \mathrm{k}\|f\|$. Thus the mapping $f \to g = Tf$ is bounded. It is obviously linear.

Let us examine a process for constructing complete orthonormal sets. We restrict ourselves to a separable nonfinite-dimensional Hilbert spaces $\mathbf{H}$ (for which the orthonormal set will be denumerable). Let $\{f_n\}$ be a set of vectors whose finite linear combinations are dense in $\mathbf{H}$. We replace the set by a subset such that any finite family of vectors in the subset is a linearly independent family. (This is done by a seriatim examination of the vectors $f_1, f_2, \cdots$ and by casting out any vector linearly dependent on the preceding ones.) We assume that this has been done and hence that the vectors of the set $\{f_n\}$ are linearly independent in this sense. We construct a set of vectors $\{g_n\}$ such that $\{g_n\}$ is a complete orthonormal set and such that for any integer $r > 0$ the subspaces spanned by $\{g_1, \cdots, g_r\}$ and $\{f_1, \cdots, f_r\}$ are identical. To this end write $g_1 = f_1/\|f_1\|$. Determine α so that $(\alpha f_1 + f_2, f_1) = 0$. Set $g_2 = h/\|h\|$ where $h = \alpha f_1 + f_2$. The construction of g_r given that $g_1, \cdots, g_{r-1}$ have already been chosen is now given by an induction argument which is not difficult to set down. Since finite linear combinations of members of the orthonormal set $\{g_n\}$ form a dense manifold in $\mathbf{H}$, $\{g_n\}$ is complete. This process is known as the Gram-Schmidt orthogonalization process.

Let us consider an application. Consider Hilbert space on the interval $[-1, 1]$:$\mathbf{L}^2_{[-1,1]}$. We note that the continuous functions on $[-1, 1]$ are dense in $\mathbf{L}^2_{[-1,1]}$ (in the norm of $\mathbf{L}^2_{[-1,1]}$) and that the polynomials are dense in the supremum norm in $\mathbf{C}_{[-1,1]}$ (by the Weierstrass theorem). Hence the polynomials are dense in $\mathbf{L}^2_{[-1,1]}$. Let $f_n(x) = x^n$, $n = 0, 1, \cdots$. Then the finite linear combinations of the f_n are dense in $\mathbf{L}^2_{[-1,1]}$. If we orthogonalize this sequence, we obtain the Legendre polynomials. Keeping in mind that $(h, k) = \int_{-1}^{1} h(x)\overline{k(x)}\,dx$, the reader may calculate the first few members of the orthonormal set $\{g_n\}$. These are, up to a constant coefficient to normalize them: $g_0(x) = 1$, $g_1(x) = x$, $g_2(x) = 1 - 3x^2$.

Let T be a bounded transformation in $\mathbf{H}$. We say that T is *normal* if it commutes with T^*: $TT^* = T^*T$. All self-adjoint and unitary transformations are normal. Notice that in any case, TT^* and T^*T are self-adjoint (and positive). We have also that for any T, $A_1 = (T + T^*)/2$ and $A_2 = (T - T^*)/2i$ are self-adjoint. Notice that $T = A_1 + iA_2$. Thus each transformation may be expressed as a linear combination of self-adjoint transformations. If T is normal, then $A_1A_2 = A_2A_1$. The converse is also true.

Let $E_{1\lambda}$ and $E_{2\mu}$ be two bounded resolutions of the identity which commute for each λ and μ: $E_{1\lambda}E_{2\mu} = E_{2\mu}E_{1\lambda}$. Suppose $A_1 = \int \lambda \, dE_{1\lambda}$ and $A_2 = \int \mu \, dE_{2\mu}$. Then $A_1A_2 = A_2A_1$ and hence $T = A_1 + iA_2$ is normal. Write $\zeta = \lambda + i\mu$ and $E_\zeta = E_{1\lambda} \cdot E_{2\mu}$. Then E_ζ is an example of a complex resolution of the identity. It may be seen that $T = \int \zeta \, dE_\zeta$ where the integration now takes place over the complex plane instead of over the real line.[6] The results of Chapter V show that conversely, every bounded normal transformation T can be so expressed.

Let E_λ be a (bounded) resolution of the identity and let $A = \int \lambda \, dE_\lambda$. If ϕ is a continuous function on the real line, it is easy to define by the methods of section 6 the integral $\int \phi(\lambda) \, dE_\lambda$ which we shall call $\phi(A)$. As before, $\phi(A)$ commutes with each transformation which commutes with E_λ, $-\infty < \lambda < \infty$. The mapping, $\phi \to \phi(A)$, is a homomorphism (sums go into sums, products go into products, complex conjugates go into adjoints) from the space of functions continuous on the line into the ring $\mathfrak{A}$(H) (we shall return to this point in section 11 of Chapter VI). In particular $\phi(A)^* = \bar{\phi}(A)$, where $\bar{\phi}$ is the complex conjugate to ϕ. It is clear that $\phi(A)$ is normal; it is self-adjoint whenever

[6] We set down the essential ideas. Let us assume that $A_1 = \int \lambda \, dE_{1\lambda}$ may be approximated as in section 6 by sums of the type $\sum_j \lambda_j' E_{1j}$ where $E_{1j} = E_1\lambda_j - E_1\lambda_{j-1}$. And, similarly, let $A_2 = \int \mu \, dE_{2\mu}$ be approximated by sums of the type $\sum_k \mu_k' E_{2k}$ with $E_{2k} = E_{2\mu_k} - E_{2\mu_{k-1}}$. Then, since $\sum_j E_{1j} = I = \sum_k E_{2k}$, $T = A_1 + iA_2$ can be approximated by sums

$$\left(\sum_j \lambda_j' E_{1j}\right) \sum_k E_{2k} + i \sum_j E_{1j} \left(\sum_k \mu_k' E_{2k}\right) = \sum_{j,k} (\lambda_j' + i\mu_k') E_{1j} E_{2k}.$$

The last sum is precisely the type of approximating sum used in defining the integral over the complex plane: $\int \zeta \, dE_\zeta$.

$\phi(\lambda)$ is real. Note that the integral given in (14) is a special case of the above situation.

To prove these various assertions, it is necessary to consider sums of the form $\sum_{i=1}^{n} \phi(\lambda_i')(E_{\lambda_i} - E_{\lambda_{i-1}})$ which approximate to $\phi(A)$.

Let E_λ be the resolution of the identity above and consider the integral $U_t = \int \exp(i\lambda t)\, dE_\lambda$. Then according to the homomorphism principle just enunciated, $U_t \cdot U_s = \int \exp(i\lambda t) \exp(i\lambda s)\, dE_\lambda = \int \exp(i\lambda(t + s))\, dE_\lambda = U_{t+s}$. We have also $U_t^* = U_{-t}$ and the family U_t is a one-parameter group of unitary transformations. Since E_λ is bounded, the group is continuous in the uniform topology of operators: $\|U_t - I\| \to 0$ as $t \to 0$.

Let us now define the *shift-operator* which throws light on a variety of questions. Let $\{q_n\}$, $n = 1, 2, \cdots$ be a complete orthonormal set in a space $\mathbf{H}$. There is a unique linear operator V such that $Vq_n = q_{n+1}$. This is the shift operator. It is obviously bounded and $\|V\| = 1$; in fact, for every f, $\|Vf\| = \|f\|$. Thus V is isometric. Its range is the closed linear manifold for which the set $\{q_n\}$, $n = 2, 3 \cdots$ is orthonormal and complete.

Let us calculate the adjoint V^* of V. We have $(V^*q_i, q_j) = (q_i, Vq_j) = (q_i, q_{j+1})$. Setting $i = 1$, this gives $V^*q_1 = 0$. If $i > 1$, clearly $V^*q_i = q_{i-1}$. Thus the null-space of V^* is one dimensional, its range is $\mathbf{H}$. The transformation V^* has no inverse and $V^*V = I$. Thus V has a left inverse and V^* has a right inverse. It is not difficult to show that the equations $(V + I)f = 0$ and $(V^* + I)g = 0$ imply $f = 0$ and $g = 0$. This implies that $(V + I)$ is $1 - 1$ from $\mathbf{H}$ onto its range and that the range is dense in $\mathbf{H}$. Call the range Δ. Then the transformation $B = i(V - I)(V + I)^{-1}$ is defined on Δ.

Let f_1 and $f_2 \in \Delta$. Write $f_1 = (V + I)h_1$ and $f_2 = (V + I)h_2$. It may be seen that $(Bf_1, f_2) = (f_1, Bf_2)$; thus B is a symmetric operator. To this end, we note that $(Bf_1, f_2) = i((V - I)h_1,$

$(V + I)h_2)$ and $(f_1, Bf_2) = -i((V + I)h_1, (V - I)h_2)$. To show equality of these two quantities, it is sufficient to use the equality, $(Vh_1, Vh_2) = (h_1, h_2)$, obtained from $V^*V = I$.

We next note that B is not self-adjoint. We shall show that q_1 belongs to the domain of B^* and $B^*q_1 = iq_1$; since $\Delta = \{f:f = (V + I)h, h \in H\}$, $q_1 \notin \Delta$. Indeed we have (as a brief computation shows), for $f \in \Delta, f = Vh + h$: $(Bf, q_1) = i((V - I)h, q_1) = ((V + I)h, iq_1) = (f, iq_1)$. Finally we show that there does not exist a symmetric transformation C which is an extension of B in the sense: $\Delta_C \supset \Delta_B$ and $B = C$ on Δ_B. (Note that Δ_B and Δ_C stand for the domains of B and C respectively.) To this end, note first that for any symmetric C, $(C + iI)f = 0$ implies $f = 0$, and if we write $(C + iI)f = g$, we have (see section 4) $\|Cf\|^2 + \|f\|^2 = \|g\|^2$. Hence $(C + iI)^{-1}$ is bounded from its range to Δ_C. Similar statements may be made for $(C - iI)$. Now returning to the problem in hand, we may see that the range of $B - iI$ is the space $\mathbf{H}$ in its entirety. Indeed, $(B - iI)f = i(V - I)h - i(V + I)h = -2ih$ where $f = (V + I)h, h \in \mathbf{H}$. Any symmetric extension C of B yields an extension $C - iI$ of $B - iI$. Since these transformations are $1 - 1$ and since the range of $B - iI$ is $\mathbf{H}$, C is an improper extension of B. Thus B is symmetric, not self-adjoint, and has no proper symmetric extensions.[7]

Let us turn briefly to a general phenomenon concerning adjoint transformations. Let T be linear and let Δ_T be dense in $\mathbf{H}$. Suppose $\Delta_{T^*} = \mathbf{H}$. Then T is bounded. The proof is easy: T^* is a closed transformation and since $\Delta_{T^*} = \mathbf{H}$, T^* is bounded (theorem 4-2 of Chapter II). Since T^* is bounded, so is T^{**}. The latter is an extension of T. Hence T is bounded.

[7] The theory of symmetric nonself-adjoint transformations is due to von Neumann.

IV SPECTRAL THEORY OF LINEAR TRANSFORMATIONS

1. The setting

We are about to enter upon a study of the structure of any bounded linear transformation defined everywhere over a general Banach space. Our first decision is to assume that the domain and range of the transformation T should be the same space **B**. The reason for this is that it is imperative for us to consider functions of T. We see right away that we may speak of polynomials in $T(T^2, T^3$, etc.) and later we shall discover that we have at our disposal a very much larger class of functions. Our second assumption is that the space **B** is complex rather than real. This will allow us to tap the resources of the Cauchy theory of analytic functions which will give us the extension hinted at immediately above: a theory of analytic functions of T.

We see therefore that given an operator T, we are to consider a family of operators associated with T containing certainly all polynomials in T and that this family is closed with respect to the formation of sums and products and hence is a ring—a little more precisely, an algebra. (Note that this algebra is commutative—a tremendously significant property.) This brings us to the second principal aspect of our problem—the algebraic aspect. We can introduce into our study an algebraic point of view and consider such ideas as those of singular element, regular element, ideal, and so on. We shall follow this path to satisfactory and, deep conclusions in the final chapter. For the present we shall be interested in phenomena which are more individual in character (structure of one element rather than a class of elements).

As we know, T is called regular if T^{-1} exists in the sense that it is bounded, linear, everywhere defined, and satisfies $TT^{-1} = T^{-1}T = I$. If T is not regular, it is called singular. Sometimes a regular element is called nonsingular. The regular element par excellence is the identity I which is its own inverse. The key to our entire study is furnished by the fact that if T is close to I, then it is regular.

Our starting point for the proof is the well-known geometric series: $(1 - x)^{-1} = 1 + x + x^2 + \cdots$, which is valid for any number x satisfying $-1 < x < 1$. Immediately we obtain from this

THEOREM 1-1: *If T satisfies $\|T\| < 1$ then $(I - T)^{-1}$ exists and*

$$(1) \qquad (I - T)^{-1} = I + T + T^2 + T^3 + \cdots,$$

the convergence of the series being in the uniform topology.

We shall look at the proof in a certain amount of detail since the argument we use recurs again and again. We lean heavily on the fact that for linear transformations A and B, $\|A + B\| \leq \|A\| + \|B\|$ and $\|A \cdot B\| \leq \|A\| \|B\|$. In particular $\|T^n\| \leq \|T\|^n$. Let $S_n = I + T + \cdots + T^n$. Then $\{S_n\}$ is a Cauchy sequence since for $n > m$ we have $\|S_n - S_m\| = \|T^{m+1} + \cdots + T^n\| \leq \|T^{m+1}\| + \cdots + \|T\|^n \leq \|T\|^{m+1}(1 + \|T\| + \|T\|^2 + \cdots) = \|T\|^{m+1}(1 - \|T\|)^{-1}$. This latter quantity may be made small at will by choosing m large since $\|T\| < 1$. Thus the series appearing on the right of (1) converges in the uniform topology. To show that the series represents $(I - T)^{-1}$, it is sufficient to multiply it by $I - T$ thus obtaining I. The multiplication term by term is validated by the fact that the series converges as just indicated.

This result has many implications, immediate and more remote. On the immediate side is the fact that we may expect at least two or three variations of (1). For example we may consider writing a series for $(A - B)^{-1}$ using the calculation $A - B =$

$A(I - A^{-1}B)$. Or again, we may have series in $(T - U)$ instead of in T. In all variations, the fundamental idea appears full grown in (1), and convergence is assured by the fact that some norm or other is less than 1.

An object which has a simple algebraic definition is that of an idempotent: $P^2 = P$. We know further the extremely important geometric interpretation associated with idempotents. And we have seen that the question of the reducibility of T is equivalent to that of finding idempotents P which commute with T. Since, in our algebra, all transformations commute, this condition will cause no difficulties. There remains the problem of generating idempotents out of T. We shall look into this further along. But we may give a hint. If C is a simple closed curve in the complex plane and if α is a point (that is, a complex number) not on C, then the integral (evaluated in the counterclockwise direction)

$$j = \frac{1}{2\pi i} \int_{C} \frac{d\zeta}{\zeta - \alpha} \tag{2}$$

has the property: $j = 0$ or $j = 1$; in any case $j^2 = j$. It is well known that $j = 1$ if and only if α is interior to C. We shall transform (2) later on by the simple expedient of replacing α by T. The integrand will then be $(\zeta I - T)^{-1}$ and theorem 1-1 will contribute to our knowledge concerning this function of ζ. Furthermore, in a very precise sense, the integral in (2), which we shall now call P instead of j, will have the property that $P = I$ on that portion of T which lies in C and $P = O$ on that portion of T which lies outside of C!

The development ahead of us involves the following components: simple algebraic notions such as regular element, idempotent, commutativity; the uniform topology; a suitable extension of the Cauchy theory of analytic functions. The simplest result involving all three fields is embodied in theorem 1-1 which states that in a given neighborhood of the identity, all transformations are regular, and their inverses are given by a power series. We turn now to the elaboration of details.

2. The spectrum

The study of the structure of T depends heavily on the behavior of the transformation $\zeta I - T$, where ζ is an arbitrary complex number. Let us introduce immediately

DEFINITION 2-1: *The resolvent set of T is the set of all complex numbers ζ such that $(\zeta I - T)^{-1}$ exists. This set is denoted by $\rho(T)$. The spectrum of T, denoted by $\sigma(T)$, is the set of all complex numbers ζ such that $(\zeta I - T)^{-1}$ fails to exist. If $\zeta \in \rho(T)$, we define the resolvent R_ζ of T by the equation*

$$R_\zeta = (\zeta I - T)^{-1}. \tag{3}$$

Clearly, the spectrum is the complement in the complex plane of the resolvent set. We shall see shortly that neither set is empty if $\mathbf{B} \neq \{0\}$. (Note that if $\mathbf{B} = \{0\}$, then $\sigma(T) = \varnothing$ since $0 = I$; also $\rho(T)$ is the entire complex plane.) That the resolvent set is not empty will be proved easily. The crucial fact that the spectrum is not empty requires much more incisive methods.

Let us now apply the methods of theorem 1-1 to the study of the resolvent set. There are two obvious extensions.

THEOREM 2-1: *Let ζ belong to the resolvent set of T, $\zeta \in \rho(T)$. Let η satisfy $|\zeta - \eta| < \|R_\zeta\|^{-1}$. Then η also is in $\rho(T)$. Thus $\rho(T)$ is an open set and $\sigma(T)$ is a closed set. Furthermore*

$$R_\eta = R_\zeta(I + (\zeta - \eta)R_\zeta + (\zeta - \eta)^2 R_\zeta^2 + \cdots). \tag{4}$$

Toward explaining the origin of the formula, write $(\eta I - T)^{-1} = [(\zeta I - T) - (\zeta - \eta)I]^{-1} = R_\zeta[I - (\zeta - \eta)R_\zeta]^{-1}$. The expansion of which theorem 1-1 is the prototype is then precisely (4) and it converges whenever $|\zeta - \eta| \, \|R_\zeta\| < 1$. This leads to the proof of the theorem. An alternative method of proof which does not pause to consider origins is this: Note first that the series in (4) is convergent in the uniform topology. Next, multiply it by $\eta I - T = (\zeta I - T) - (\zeta - \eta)I$ thus obtaining I.

THEOREM 2-2: *If ζ satisfies $|\zeta| > \|T\|$, then $\zeta \in \rho(T)$. Thus, the resolvent set of T is not empty. For such a ζ,*

$$R_\zeta = \zeta^{-1}(I + \zeta^{-1}T + \zeta^{-2}T^2 + \cdots). \tag{5}$$

The formula (5) is obtained by writing $(\zeta I - T)^{-1} = \zeta^{-1}(I - \zeta^{-1}T)^{-1}$ and proceeding with the series development of theorem 1-1. Convergence is then assured in case $\|\zeta^{-1}T\| < 1$, that is, $|\zeta| > \|T\|$.

This theorem states that $\sigma(T)$ is contained in the disc $|\zeta| \leq \|T\|$. The smallest disc centered at the origin which covers the spectrum is particularly important and will be studied in detail later (see *spectral radius*).

We introduce now the famous functional equation for the resolvent, known since the first days of integral equations.

THEOREM 2-3: *If ζ and η belong to the resolvent set of T, then*

$$R_\zeta - R_\eta = (\eta - \zeta)R_\zeta R_\eta. \tag{6}$$

The resolvent R_ζ commutes with every transformation which commutes with T.

The verification of (6) is obtained by multiplying both sides by $(\zeta I - T)(\eta I - T)$—noting, of course, that this multiplier is a regular transformation. As for the assertion on commutativity, note that if S commutes with T, it commutes with $\zeta I - T$ and hence with R_ζ.

Before closing this section, let us make a few remarks. A few authors define the resolvent by $R_\zeta = (T - \zeta I)^{-1}$. It seems that our course is preferable since the usual formulas of the Cauchy theory are linked to our definition. More seriously: The older literature on integral equations defines the resolvent by $R_\zeta = (I - \zeta T)^{-1}$. The transformation necessary to proceed from this definition to the one given earlier is quite elementary but very annoying. Thus the reader is urged to check on this point before making comparisons between treatises.

3. Integration procedures

We develop now a theory of integration of functions $S(\zeta)$ which are defined for suitable sets of complex numbers ζ and whose values are bounded linear transformations. The path of integration will be an appropriate curve C in the complex plane. The integral which we shall define presently (and briefly) will be denoted by $\int_C S(\zeta)\, d\zeta$. We note in passing that all integration procedures call for the taking of limits; in the present instance, the limit will be taken in the uniform (hence the easiest) topology of operators.

Let $\zeta = \zeta(t)$, $0 \leq t \leq 1$, be the equation of a rectifiable curve C in the complex plane. Let $S(\zeta)$ be a transformation for each ζ where ζ belongs to some given set of complex numbers (for example, an open set) and let the map $\zeta \to S(\zeta)$ be continuous in the uniform topology. We note that if the curve C lies in the set of definition of $S(\zeta)$, then $S(\zeta(t))$ is a continuous function of t, $0 \leq t \leq 1$. (We shall be interested only in the case in which the transformations $S(\zeta)$ commute with each other.)

Now let $0 = t_0 \leq t_1 \leq \cdots \leq t_n = 1$ be a partition of the unit interval. Write $\zeta_i = \zeta(t_i)$ and $\Delta\zeta_i = \zeta_i - \zeta_{i-1}$. Furthermore, let t_i' satisfy $t_{i-1} \leq t_i' \leq t_i$ and write $\zeta_i' = \zeta(t_i')$. Form the sum $\sum_{i=1}^{n} S(\zeta_i')\, \Delta\zeta_i$. It is easy to show that these Riemann type sums converge in the sense of integration to a limit. This limit is independent of the particular parametrization chosen to represent the curve C. Let us write $S = \int_C S(\zeta)\, d\zeta$ for this limit. Speaking rapidly, the existence of the limit S means that for a given $\epsilon > 0$, there exists a $\delta > 0$ such that if $t_i - t_{i-1} < \delta$, then $\left\| S - \sum_{i=1}^{n} S(\zeta_i')\, \Delta\zeta_i \right\| < \epsilon$.

Note that the map $t \to \|S(\zeta(t)\|$ is continuous. Hence on the closed interval $[0, 1]$, $\|S(\zeta(t)\| \leq K$ where K is a suitable constant. Let l_C represent the length of the curve C. Then clearly we

have $\left\| \sum_{i=1}^{n} S(\zeta_i') \, \Delta\zeta_i \right\| \leq \sum_{i=1}^{n} \|S(\zeta_i')\| \, |\Delta\zeta_i| \leq \mathrm{K} \sum_{i=1}^{n} |\Delta\zeta_i| \leq \mathrm{K} l_{\mathrm{C}}$.
Hence $\|S\| \leq \mathrm{K} l_{\mathrm{C}}$.

Finally, we note that S commutes with every transformation which commutes with each $S(\zeta)$.

4. The fundamental projections

We introduce now the fundamental projection which is the key to the study of the structure of a general transformation T. Up to the present the notion of analytic function has presented itself in the form of infinite series such as appear in (1), (4), and (5). Now, we shall introduce the integrals along curves which are so characteristic of the Cauchy theory.[1]

Let T be a bounded linear transformation and let $R_\zeta = (\zeta I - T)^{-1}$ be its resolvent, defined in the set $\rho(T)$ of the complex plane. As we have seen (theorems 2-1 and 2-2), $\rho(T)$ is a non-empty open set. For every ζ in $\rho(T)$, R_ζ is a bounded linear transformation and the map $\zeta \to R_\zeta$ is continuous. This last fact is an easy deduction to be made from equation (4): if $|\eta - \zeta|$ is small, then $\|R_\eta - R_\zeta\|$ is small.

Let C be a curve lying entirely in $\rho(T)$; let C be defined by $\zeta = \zeta(t)$. Then, in accordance with our discussion of integration, the transformation $\int_{\mathrm{C}} R_\zeta \, d\zeta$ is well defined. Consider now two curves C_0 and C_1 and let us suppose that C_1 is obtained from C_0 by a slight deformation which leaves the end points fixed. It is understood that the deformation at no stage carries the curve outside of $\rho(T)$. The proper language for expressing our notions comes from homotopy theory. Since there are no essential difficulties, we shall proceed very swiftly. We are considering a one-parameter system of curves C_s: $\zeta = \zeta_s(t)$, $0 \leq s \leq 1$, where the functions $\zeta_s(t)$ are endowed with obvious continuity proper-

[1] The author's theory of reducibility reproduced in this section was published in 1942.

ties and the values $s = 0$, $s = 1$ gives us the initial and terminal curves of the deformation process. We shall say that C_1 is obtained from C_0 by an allowable deformation. Our first result follows.

THEOREM 4-1: *Let T be a transformation, R_ζ its resolvent, $\zeta \in \rho(T)$. Let C_0 be a rectifiable curve lying in $\rho(T)$ and let C_1 be a curve in $\rho(T)$ which is obtained from C_0 by an allowable deformation. Then*

$$\int_{C_0} R_\zeta \, d\zeta = \int_{C_1} R_\zeta \, d\zeta. \tag{7}$$

Proof: The diagram (Figure 1) indicates the situation. The curves C_{s_1} and C_{s_2} are two "general adjacent" positions of the curve C_s

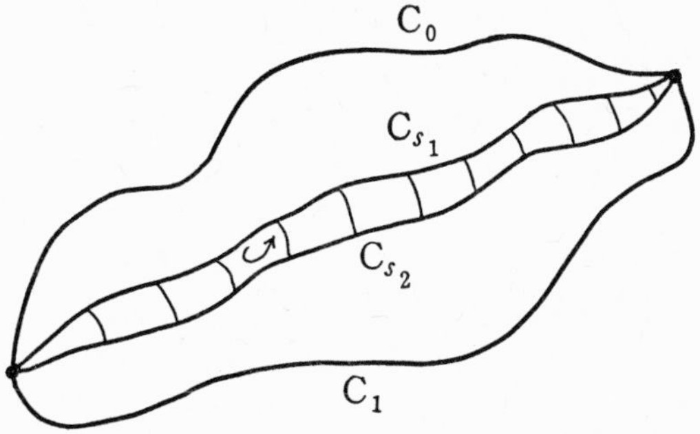

Figure 1.

in the process of deformation. We shall indicate how to prove that the integral of R_ζ over C_{s_1} is equal to that over C_{s_2}. The formula (7) is then obtained by "hopping" from C_0 to C_1 through a finite number of intermediate curves and applying this result.

We may introduce on C_{s_1} a certain number of points and follow these points as C_{s_1} is deformed into C_{s_2}. The result is the ladder indicated in the diagram. If we now integrate R_ζ around each little rectangle of the ladder and add the results, the contributions of the rungs cancel and what is left is the difference of the integrals along C_{s_1} and C_{s_2}.

To show that the integrals along C_{s_1} and C_{s_2} are equal, it is sufficient to prove that the integral around each little rectangle of the ladder is zero. This latter conclusion can be derived from formula (4). Let ζ be a fixed point of some rectangle Q. Suppose that the rectangle is so small that the series (4) is valid for every point of it. Then

$$(8) \qquad \int_Q R_\eta \, d\eta = \int_Q R_\zeta \, d\eta + \int_Q (\zeta - \eta) R_\zeta^2 \, d\eta + \cdots$$

and each of the integrals on the right-hand side is zero by the classic Cauchy theory of analytic functions.

To carry out the details of the proof rigorously it is necessary to appeal to the uniform continuity and the boundedness of continuous functions defined on compact sets. We shall not give the details here.

Suppose now that the curve C_0 is closed and that C_1 represents any closed curve obtained from C_0 by an allowable deformation, including now the movement of the initial end point. Then clearly the same result is valid.

A corollary of the above theorem is so important that it will be stated here separately although it will come out again later in connection with the projection theory.

THEOREM 4-2: *The spectrum of T is not empty unless the underlying space has dimension zero (consists of the element 0 only).*

Suppose the spectrum of T is empty. Let C_s, $0 \leq s \leq 1$, represent a circle of radius $2s\|T\|$ with center the origin. For $s = 0$, we see that $\int_{C_0} R_\zeta \, d\zeta = O$. For $s = 1$, we have a circle of radius $2\|T\|$ and we may replace R_ζ by the series expansion in (5). The integration may be carried out term by term. All terms after the first give O. The first term gives $2\pi i I$ (all this, by the classic Cauchy theory). Now, according to the preceding theorem, the integrals around C_0 and C_1 are equal, for by hypothesis, T has no spectrum and the deformation from C_0 to C_1 is allowable. Therefore $2\pi i I = O$. This means that if $f \in \mathbf{B}$, $f = 0$. Hence $\mathbf{B}$ has dimension zero.

As we shall see later, this result is fundamental to the entire theory of Banach algebras. Let us now proceed to the definition of the fundamental projection.

THEOREM 4-3: *Let* C *be a simple closed rectifiable curve which lies in the resolvent set* $\rho(T)$ *of* T. *Let*

$$P = \frac{1}{2\pi i} \int_{C} R_\zeta \, d\zeta. \tag{9}$$

Then P *is a projection* ($P^2 = P$), *which commutes with every transformation which commutes with* T. *In particular, the pair of closed linear manifolds associated with* P *reduces* T.

The reader should note that although C lies in $\rho(T)$, the spectrum $\sigma(T)$ will in general have points both inside C and outside C.

The commutativity properties follow from theorem 2-3 and from our discussion of integration. Also, if $P^2 = P$ and $PT = TP$, then the closed linear manifolds associated with P clearly reduce T (as is shown in theorem 6-4 of Chapter II). We now prove that $P^2 = P$.

We propose to square the integral in (9). However, before doing so, we shall construct a simple closed curve C′ which lies entirely inside C and which is obtained from C by a slight allowable [within $\rho(T)$] deformation. By theorem 4-1, $\int_C R_\zeta \, d\zeta = \int_{C'} R_\zeta \, d\zeta$. Thus we have

$$\begin{aligned}(2\pi i)^2 P^2 &= \int_C R_\eta \, d\eta \cdot \int_{C'} R_\zeta \, d\zeta \\ &= \int_C \int_{C'} (R_\zeta - R_\eta)(\eta - \zeta)^{-1} \, d\eta \, d\zeta \\ &= \int_{C'} R_\zeta \int_C (\eta - \zeta)^{-1} \, d\eta \, d\zeta - \int_C R_\eta \int_{C'} (\eta - \zeta)^{-1} \, d\zeta \, d\eta \\ &= 2\pi i \int_{C'} R_\zeta \, d\zeta - O = (2\pi i)^2 P.\end{aligned} \tag{10}$$

A look at figure 2 will help to keep straight the calculations.

In formula (10) we have used the functional equation of the resolvent (6) and the classic fact that an integral of the form $\int_C (\alpha - \beta)^{-1}\, d\alpha$ is $2\pi i$ if β lies within C and is 0 if β lies outside of C.

THEOREM 4-4: *Let* C *and* C′ *be two simple closed rectifiable curves lying in the resolvent set* $\rho(T)$ *of* T. *Let* P *and* P' *be the projections associated to* C *and* C′ *by means of formula* (9). *Then* $PP' = O$ *in the case* C *and* C′ *each lie exterior to the other;* $PP' = P'$ *if* C′ *lies interior to* C.

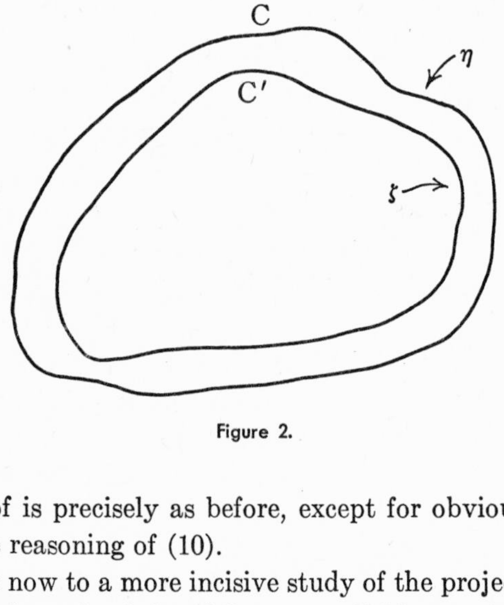

Figure 2.

The proof is precisely as before, except for obvious modifications in the reasoning of (10).

We come now to a more incisive study of the projection P. Let $\{\mathbf{M}, \mathbf{N}\}$ be the pair of closed linear manifolds associated with P. Since $PT = TP$, $T(\mathbf{M}) \subset \mathbf{M}$ and $T(\mathbf{N}) \subset \mathbf{N}$. Thus we may consider the transformation T restricted to $\mathbf{M}$ and to $\mathbf{N}$. Let us write T' for the restriction of T to $\mathbf{M}$ and T'' for the restriction of T to $\mathbf{N}$. In the same way we can restrict P obtaining the transformations P' and P''. We note that $P' = I'$ and $P'' = O''$ where I' and O'' are the identity and zero transformations on $\mathbf{M}$ and $\mathbf{N}$ respectively.

Since $R_\zeta P = PR_\zeta$ for $\zeta \in \rho(T)$ we may introduce the transformations R'_ζ and R''_ζ. For $f \in \mathbf{M}$ we have $R'_\zeta(\zeta I' - T') f = f$, that is, $R'_\zeta(\zeta I' - T') = I'$. Similarly, we show that $R''_\zeta(\zeta I'' - T'') = I''$. We may state the result as follows: If $\zeta \in \rho(T)$, then $\zeta \in \rho(T')$ and $\zeta \in \rho(T'')$. Furthermore, the transformations R'_ζ and R''_ζ are precisely the resolvent transformations of T' and T''.

We consider the converse situation. Let $\zeta \in \rho(T')$ and $\zeta \in \rho(T'')$. Let A' and A'' be the transformations which satisfy $A'(\zeta I' - T') = I'$, $A''(\zeta I'' - T'') = I''$. Then there exists a unique bounded linear transformation A (defined in **B**) whose restrictions to **M** and **N** are A' and A'' respectively. (If $f \in \mathbf{B}$, Af is defined by $Af = A'Pf + A''(I - P)f$.) We have $A(\zeta I - T)f = f$ for each f in **M** and each f in **N**. Since $\mathbf{B} = \mathbf{M} \oplus \mathbf{N}$, this gives $A(\zeta I - T) = I$. Thus $\zeta \in \rho(T)$ and $A = R_\zeta$. This shows immediately that $A' = R'_\zeta$ and $A'' = R''_\zeta$.

We may state our conclusions slightly differently: A number ζ is in the spectrum of T if and only if it is in the spectrum of one of the transformations T' or T''.

We come now to the crucial property of the projection P. We shall show that if ζ lies outside of the curve C, then ζ belongs to the resolvent set of T'. That is, $\rho(T')$ contains the exterior of C. Similarly, we shall show that if ζ lies interior to C, then ζ belongs to the resolvent set of T''. These facts and the preceding paragraphs then demonstrate that the spectrum of T' consists precisely of that portion of the spectrum of T which lies inside C. Also, the spectrum of T'' consists precisely of that portion of the spectrum of T which lies outside C.

To demonstrate the above assertion—that the exterior of C lies in the resolvent set of T'—we must show that if ζ is exterior to C, then there exists a transformation A' such that $A'(\zeta I' - T') = I'$. We shall show this, but in an altered form. We shall show instead that there exists a transformation A defined in **B** which commutes with T and which is reduced by the pair $\{\mathbf{M}, \mathbf{N}\}$ such that $A(\zeta I - T) = P$. This will imply that $A'(\zeta I' - T') = P' = I'$, and hence, that $\zeta \in \rho(T')$.

To this end, consider first the trivial identity

(11) $(\zeta I - T)R_\eta = (\eta I - T)R_\eta + (\zeta - \eta)R_\eta = I + (\zeta - \eta)R_\eta.$

We have therefore

$$(12)\quad \begin{aligned}&(\zeta I - T)\cdot\frac{1}{2\pi i}\int_{\mathrm{C}} R_\eta(\zeta - \eta)^{-1}\,d\eta \\ &= \frac{1}{2\pi i}\int_{\mathrm{C}}(\zeta - \eta)^{-1}\,d\eta\cdot I + \frac{1}{2\pi i}\int_{\mathrm{C}} R_\eta\,d\eta = O + P = P.\end{aligned}$$

This proves then that $(\zeta I' - T')^{-1}$ exists. Suppose now that ζ lies interior to C. Then the integral in (12) equals $-I + P$. The restriction of this transformation to the manifold **N** gives $-I''$. Thus $(\zeta I'' - T'')^{-1}$ exists. We collect these results in

THEOREM 4-5: *Let T be a bounded linear transformation. Let* C *be a simple closed curve lying in $\rho(T)$. Let P be the projection*

$$P = \frac{1}{2\pi i}\int_{\mathrm{C}} R_\zeta\,d\zeta$$

associated with T and C. *Let* {**M**, **N**} *be the pair of linear manifolds associated with P. Let T' and T'' represent the restrictions of T to* **M** *and* **N** *respectively. Then the spectrum of T' is precisely that subset of the spectrum of T which lies in the interior of* C. *The spectrum of T'' is precisely that subset of the spectrum of T which lies in the exterior of* C.

We derive one more important property of the transformation P.

THEOREM 4-6: *For the projection P of formula* (9), $P = O$ *if and only if the interior of the curve* C *belongs to the resolvent set of T. Similarly, $P = I$ if and only if the spectrum of T lies entirely interior to* C.

We have touched on aspects of this earlier. Suppose $P = O$. Then $\mathbf{M} = \{O\}$ and $\mathbf{N} = \mathbf{B}$. Thus $T'' = T$. Now, according to the preceding theorem, the spectrum of T'' lies exterior to C. Hence the spectrum of T lies exterior to C; that is, the interior of C belongs to the resolvent set of T. Next, suppose that the interior of C belongs to the resolvent set of T. Then C may be deformed to a point within $\rho(T)$. Since P is a constant under this deformation, $P = O$.

Now, suppose that for the curve C, $P = I$. Then $\mathbf{M} = \mathbf{B}$ and $\mathbf{N} = \{O\}$. Thus $T' = T$. Now, according to the preceding theorem, the spectrum of T' lies interior to C. Thus the exterior of C belongs to the resolvent set of T. Next, suppose that the exterior of C belongs to the resolvent set of T. Then C may be deformed in an allowable manner into the circle $|\zeta| = 2\|T\|$. This deformation does not change the value of P. But, as we have seen, the integral (9) over this circle gives the value I. Thus $P = I$. This proves the theorem.

Before we terminate this section, let us point out that in accordance with theorem 4-5, the projection P is a function not of the curve C but rather of the domain of the complex plane whose boundary is C. To make our ideas more precise, consider for a given transformation T the circle $|\zeta| = 2\|T\|$. Within this fundamental set [which contains all of $\sigma(T)$] consider any open set (domain) G whose boundary ∂G consists of a finite number of simple rectifiable curves lying in $\rho(T)$, each curve of the boundary being provided with a sense. Then we may consider instead of (9) the integral $(2\pi i)^{-1} \int_{\partial G} R_\zeta \, d\zeta$. It is easy to establish for this integral the appropriate theorems—which involve small variations at most from the ones given in the text: theorems 4-1 to 4-6. We leave it to the reader to rephrase these various results in the new context.

5. A special case

We consider now a special case of the preceding theory.[2] Let T be such that $\rho(T)$ contains the circle Γ: $|\zeta| = 1$. We propose to calculate the projection P which corresponds to Γ. We shall see that the calculation can be made easily with the help of long-

[2] See footnote 1.

known facts concerning the complex roots of unity. The results for this special case lead to the principal theorem concerning the spectral radius of T.

We propose to calculate the integral $(2\pi i)^{-1} \int_\Gamma R_\zeta \, d\zeta$ where Γ is the circle: $|\zeta| = 1$. We remind the reader that such an integral is a limit of a type of Riemann sum and we propose to calculate it by considering a particular type of approximating sum. Let n be a positive integer and let $\alpha = \exp (2\pi i)/n$. We subdivide the circle Γ into n parts by means of the points $\alpha^0, \alpha^1, \cdots, \alpha^n$ and corresponding to this subdivision consider the Riemann sum

$$(13) \qquad (2\pi i)^{-1} \sum_{j=0}^{n-1} (\alpha^j I - T)^{-1}(\alpha^{j+1} - \alpha^j).$$

We rewrite this sum in the form

$$(2\pi i)^{-1} \sum_{j=0}^{n-1} (I - \alpha^{-j}T)^{-1}(\alpha - 1) = (2\pi i)^{-1} n(\alpha - 1)(I - T^n)^{-1}.$$

In obtaining the latter expression we have made use of elementary properties of the nth roots of unity (in particular, the partial fraction decomposition for $(x^n - 1)^{-1}$). Now since the derivative with respect to x of $\exp (2\pi ix)$ at $x = 0$ equals $2\pi i$, it follows immediately that $n(\alpha - 1) \to 2\pi i$ as $n \to \infty$. Since the sum (13) tends to P as $n \to \infty$ we obtain

THEOREM 5-1: *Let Γ be the circle $|\zeta| = 1$ and suppose Γ lies in $\rho(T)$. Then for the projection P associated to Γ by formula* (9) *we have*

$$(14) \qquad P = \lim_{n \to \infty} (I - T^n)^{-1}.$$

Suppose now that $\sigma(T)$ lies entirely within Γ. In this case we have (according to theorem 4-6) $P = I$. Thus $(I - T^n)^{-1}$

$\to I$ and hence $(I - T^n) \to I$, that is, $T^n \to O$. It follows that $\|T^n\| \to 0$.

6. The spectral radius

The above result is fundamental to the computation of the spectral radius. But first a definition. We have seen that for any transformation T, the set $|\zeta| > \|T\|$ is a subset of the resolvent set, $\rho(T)$. Thus the spectrum of T is bounded.

DEFINITION 6-1: *The number* $r_T = \sup_{\zeta \in \sigma(T)} |\zeta|$ *is called the spectral radius of* T.

In all cases $r_T \leq \|T\|$. We shall now establish the fundamental formula for r_T which was given by Gelfand.

Let $r_T < 1$. Then as we have seen in the preceding section $\|T^n\| \to 0$. This means that for n large, $\|T^n\| < 1$ and $\|T^n\|^{1/n} < 1$. Thus $\limsup_{n\to\infty} \|T^n\|^{1/n} \leq 1$. Now let T be arbitrary. For $\epsilon > 0$ write $S = (r_T + \epsilon)^{-1}T$. Then $r_S < 1$ and by the preceding, $\limsup_{n\to\infty} \|S^n\|^{1/n} \leq 1$. This gives immediately (remembering that $\epsilon > 0$ is arbitrary) $\limsup_{n\to\infty} \|T^n\|^{1/n} \leq r_T$.

If $\mathcal{E}$ is a set of complex numbers, then $\mathcal{E}^n$ represents the set of all μ such that $\mu = \lambda^n$, $\lambda \in \mathcal{E}$.

THEOREM 6-1: *For any transformation* T,

$$\sigma(T^n) = [\sigma(T)]^n.$$

Suppose first that $\lambda \in \sigma(T)$, that is, $(\lambda I - T)$ has no inverse. Then since

$$(14) \quad \lambda^n I - T^n = (\lambda I - T)(\lambda^{n-1}I + \lambda^{n-2}T + \cdots + T^{n-1}),$$

and noting that the factors in (14) commute, it is clear that $\lambda^n I - T^n$ has no inverse. Thus $\lambda^n \in \sigma(T^n)$ or $[\sigma(T)]^n \subset \sigma(T^n)$.

Conversely, let $\mu \in \sigma(T^n)$ and let λ be an nth root of μ. Then a factorization of $\lambda^n I - T^n$ shows that for at least one such λ, $\lambda \in \sigma(T)$. This implies that $\sigma(T^n) \subset [\sigma(T)]^n$ and the theorem is proved.

The theorem implies that $r_{T^n} = (r_T)^n$. Now clearly $r_{T^n} \leq \|T^n\|$. Hence $r_T \leq \|T^n\|^{1/n}$. This implies $r_T \leq \liminf_{n\to\infty} \|T^n\|^{1/n}$. We put together our various inequalities:

$$r_T \leq \liminf_{n\to\infty} \|T^n\|^{1/n} \leq \limsup_{n\to\infty} \|T^n\|^{1/n} \leq r_T. \tag{15}$$

We have therefore proved the spectral radius theorem:

THEOREM 6-2: *For any transformation T, the sequence $\{\|T^n\|^{1/n}\}$ converges and its limit is r_T:*

$$r_T = \lim_{n\to\infty} \|T^n\|^{1/n}. \tag{16}$$

7. Analytic functions of operators

We have observed many times before that, for any bounded linear transformation T, we may construct the integral powers T^n, $n > 0$, and also the polynomials in T. More generally, we may consider rational functions of T providing the denominators are regular. We note that, in this way, we obtain a mapping from functions (rational for the moment) f to operators which are naturally indicated by the symbol $f(T)$. This mapping has certain obvious properties (it is a ring homomorphism). This mapping is called an operational calculus. We shall establish the theory of this calculus below. In particular we shall show that we may consider analytic functions of T such as exp (T) and sometimes arctan (T). The possibility of developing such a calculus for infinite dimensional spaces was first pointed out by F. Riesz. The results are obtained by a judicious mixture of the classic Cauchy theory, especially the Cauchy formula, the functional equation of the resolvent, and elementary facts concerning the spectrum.

Let G be a region of the complex plane (connected open set) and suppose G contains the spectrum of T: $\sigma(T) \subset$ G. Let C be a simple closed rectifiable curve lying in G and containing $\sigma(T)$ in its interior. Let $f(\zeta)$ be a function which is analytic in G—that is, at every point $\zeta \in$ G, the derivative $f'(\zeta)$ exists. We recall that we have developed an operator-valued theory of Riemann integration in section 3. The integral $(2\pi i)^{-1} \int_C f(\zeta) R_\zeta \, d\zeta$ is well defined and will be denoted by $f(T)$.[3] We write therefore

$$f(T) = \frac{1}{2\pi i} \int_C \frac{f(\zeta)}{\zeta I - T} \, d\zeta. \tag{17}$$

We note first of all that if C is deformed into a curve C′ in an allowable fashion (see section 4), the integral (17) remains constant during the deformation. The argument for this is precisely that given earlier (see theorem 4-1). Thus the operator $f(T)$ is independent of C; it depends only on T and on $f(\zeta)$.[4]

We see also that if $f_1(\zeta)$ and $f_2(\zeta)$ are functions analytic in regions G_1 and G_2 respectively, both of which contain the set $\sigma(T)$, then we may in (17) restrict ourselves to a common region $G = G_1 \cap G_2$ in which both functions are analytic, and, more important, in which $f_1(\zeta) + f_2(\zeta)$ and $f_1(\zeta) \cdot f_2(\zeta)$ are analytic. Suppose $g(\zeta) = f_1(\zeta) + f_2(\zeta)$. Then it is clear from the linearity of the integration process that the operator $g(T)$ corresponding to $g(\zeta)$ is the sum of the two operators $f_1(T)$ and $f_2(T)$. Similarly, if $h(\zeta) = f_1(\zeta) \cdot f_2(\zeta)$, then the operator $h(T)$ is the product of the two operators $f_1(T)$ and $f_2(T)$. The proof of this fact is more difficult and is given below.

Let $f_1(T)$ be evaluated by an integral around a suitable curve C_1. As for $f_2(T)$, let it be evaluated by an integral around a curve C_2 which lies entirely in the interior of C_1. As we calculate, we

[3] The formula was proposed by F. Riesz and was elaborated by Gelfand and Dunford.

[4] We have not, above, and shall not always, in the future, adhere to the proper notation for functions, namely, f [rather than $f(\zeta)$]. This lapse from good usage is particularly common in dealing with analytic functions.

remember (and use!) the functional equation for the resolvent [see (6)].

We have

$$
\begin{aligned}
f_1(T) \cdot f_2(T) &= (2\pi i)^{-2} \int_{C_1} f_1(\zeta) R_\zeta \, d\zeta \int_{C_2} f_2(\eta) R_\eta \, d\eta \\
&= (2\pi i)^{-2} \int_{C_1} \int_{C_2} f_1(\zeta) f_2(\eta) R_\zeta R_\eta \, d\zeta \, d\eta \\
&= (2\pi i)^{-2} \int_{C_1} f_1(\zeta) R_\zeta \int_{C_2} \frac{f_2(\eta)}{\eta - \zeta} \, d\eta \, d\zeta \qquad (18) \\
&\quad + (2\pi i)^{-2} \int_{C_2} f_2(\eta) R_\eta \int_{C_1} \frac{f_1(\zeta)}{\zeta - \eta} \, d\zeta \, d\eta \\
&= O + (2\pi i)^{-1} \int_{C_2} f_2(\eta) f_1(\eta) R_\eta \, d\eta = h(T).
\end{aligned}
$$

In the operational calculus which we are developing, we see that if $f(\zeta) = 1$ for all ζ, then the integral (17) reduces to that considered in (9) and since C contains the spectrum of T in its interior, $f(T) = I$. We see also that if $f(\zeta) = \zeta$ for all ζ, then $f(T) = T$. For, since $I = (2\pi i)^{-1} \int_C R_\zeta \, d\zeta$, we have $T = (2\pi i)^{-1} \int_C T R_\zeta \, d\zeta$. Thus [remembering that $f(\zeta) = \zeta$],

$$
\begin{aligned}
f(T) - T &= (2\pi i)^{-1} \int_C \zeta R_\zeta \, d\zeta - (2\pi i)^{-1} \int_C T R_\zeta \, d\zeta \\
&= (2\pi i)^{-1} \int_C (\zeta I - T) R_\zeta \, d\zeta \qquad (19) \\
&= (2\pi i)^{-1} \int_C I \, d\zeta = O.
\end{aligned}
$$

By virtue of the multiplication property proved above, we see right away that if $f(\zeta) = \zeta^n$, then $f(T) = T^n$ and, in general, if $f(\zeta)$ is a polynomial, then $f(T)$ as given by (17) is precisely the operator given by the more naïve processes which we have used earlier on many occasions.

We are ready to summarize all our results into the form of a theorem,

THEOREM 7-1: *Let T be a bounded linear operator with spectrum $\sigma(T)$. Let* A *be the algebra of functions $f(\zeta)$ analytic in a region which includes $\sigma(T)$. Then the formula* (17) *is a homomorphic map of* A *into the set* $\mathfrak{A}$(B) *of all operators of* B *into* B. *Under the homomorphism: $f(\zeta) \rightarrow f(T)$, we have $1 \rightarrow I$ and $\zeta \rightarrow T$.*

It is needless to say that all operators $f(T)$ commute with all operators which commute with T. It should be pointed out that in order to eliminate difficulties of a topological nature, we have essentially assumed that the analytic functions under consideration are defined in a convex region which contains the spectrum of the transformation.

A final word. We could have considered, had we so desired, open sets G, containing $\sigma(T)$, whose boundary ∂G consists of a finite number of simple rectifiable curves. For this situation, we replace $\int_C$ by $\int_{\partial G}$. This method allows us to consider sets which are not necessarily connected. We then consider functions $f(\zeta)$ which are analytic in each connected component of G. We leave it to the reader to show that the results in this case can be obtained by mixing the methods of this section with those of section 4. In fact, an examination of the situation reveals that in these theories we have two variables: the function $f(\zeta)$ and the curve C. In the present section, $f(\zeta)$ varies over analytic functions while C constantly has $\sigma(T)$ in its interior. In section 4 on projections, $f(\zeta) = 1$ and C is allowed to vary in all possible ways. The two developments are quite distinct.

V THE STRUCTURE OF SELF-ADJOINT TRANSFORMATIONS

1. Preliminary discussion

In this chapter we develop the structure theory for self-adjoint transformations in Hilbert space **H**. If A is such a transformation, its structure is summarized by the integral representation

$$A = \int \lambda \, dE_\lambda, \tag{1}$$

where E_λ is the resolution of the identity associated to A. The treatment which we give is valid for all cases, bounded or unbounded. It is given precisely as we published it over a decade ago.[1] The basic ideas for the proof come from the general calculus of residues as developed in the last chapter. As we have seen, the residue calculus involves integration along curves which lie in the resolvent set of A. We have seen also (theorem 4-2 of Chapter III) that the resolvent set of A includes all complex numbers which are off the real axis. The projection theory of the last chapter (in particular, theorem 4-5) suggests that we may calculate E_λ by taking simple closed curves C which cut the real axis at two points. Thus, if C cuts the real line at λ_1 and λ_2 with $\lambda_1 < \lambda_2$ then the projection P associated to C should equal $E_{\lambda_2} - E_{\lambda_1}$. This method can only be applied in case λ_1 and λ_2 both lie in the resolvent set of A, for in that case, all of C is in the

[1] In the Szeged Acta (1950), dedicated to the seventieth anniversary of F. Riesz and L. Fejer.

resolvent set. Our main task will be to devise alternatives in order to be able to cut through the spectrum itself thus obtaining the value of $E_{\lambda_2} - E_{\lambda_1}$ for all pairs λ_1, λ_2. This will be done by means of an operational calculus which is quite interesting in its own right and seems to have possibilities which go much beyond the calls we make upon it.[2]

In the development of our method, the possible presence of the point spectrum (defined below) causes annoyance. For that reason, we herd it together and clean it out. This means that we show that there exists a closed linear manifold $\mathbf{M}$ such that $A(\mathbf{M}) \subset \mathbf{M}$, $A(\mathbf{M}^{\perp}) \subset \mathbf{M}^{\perp}$ and that A is self-adjoint in $\mathbf{M}$ and in $\mathbf{M}^{\perp}$. Furthermore, in $\mathbf{M}$, A has a pure point spectrum and in $\mathbf{M}^{\perp}$, A has no point spectrum. Transformations with pure point spectrum are in many ways trivial to handle; it is the continuous spectrum that calls for depth. Thus, in order to establish formula (1), it will be sufficient to do so for the two spaces $\mathbf{M}$ and $\mathbf{M}^{\perp}$. The results obtained can then be "put together" to obtain the requisite formula for $\mathbf{H}$. Our treatment implies that $\mathbf{H}$ is a complex space.

In order to carry through our program, we have to give a brief discussion of the notion of positiveness for self-adjoint operators A. This we do at the very beginning, restricting ourselves for convenience to bounded operators. The existence of this notion is very characteristic of the entire theory and our fundamental results will be described directly in its terms.

2. Positive operators

Throughout this section we consider only bounded self-adjoint operators. We introduce once more and study more thoroughly a notion which came up earlier (see definition 6-2 of Chapter III).

DEFINITION 2-1: *If A is bounded and self-adjoint, we write $A \geq O$ (read: A is positive) is case for all* $f \in \mathbf{H}$

[2] The reader may wish to note that the material of this chapter is not used in the next one until the last section on applications.

$$(Af, f) \geq 0.$$

We note rapidly that if $A \geq O$ and $B \geq O$, then $A + B \geq O$; also $\lambda A \geq O$ for $\lambda \geq 0$. We write $A \geq B$ in case $A - B \geq O$. We see quickly that this introduces a partial ordering in the real Banach space of all self-adjoint transformations. Clearly, $A \geq A$; and $A \geq B$ along with $B \geq C$ implies $A \geq C$. We show that if $A \geq B$ and $B \geq A$, then $A = B$.

Setting $C = A - B$, we have $C \geq O$ and $-C \geq O$. This means that for all f, $(Cf, f) = 0$. We give to f in turn the values: g, h, $g + h$, and $g + ih$. This shows finally that $(Cg, h) = 0$ for all $g, h \in \mathbf{H}$ and hence $C = O$.

THEOREM 2-1: *If the bounded self-adjoint transformation A satisfies $A \geq I$, then A^{-1} exists and $\|A^{-1}\| \leq 1$.*

Since $A \geq I$, we have

$$\|Af\| \, \|f\| \geq (Af, f) \geq (f, f) = \|f\|^2 \tag{2}$$

for all f in $\mathbf{H}$ and hence in particular

$$\|Af\| \geq \|f\|. \tag{3}$$

Thus $Af = O$ implies $f = O$. Hence A is a 1-1 transformation from $\mathbf{H}$ to its range and the transformation A^{-1} defined on the range of A satisfies $\|A^{-1}\| \leq 1$.

Now, the range of A is dense in $\mathbf{H}$. For, if there is an element f which is orthogonal to Ag for all g, we have $0 = (f, Ag) = (Af, g)$ and hence $Af = O$. Thus $f = O$ and the range of A is dense in $\mathbf{H}$.

We show that the range of A is all of $\mathbf{H}$. Suppose that $g \in \mathbf{H}$ and that $\{f_n\}$ is so chosen that $Af_n \to g$. Then since $\|Af_n - Af_m\| = \|A(f_n - f_m)\| \geq \|f_n - f_m\|$ by (3), we see that $\{f_n\}$ is a Cauchy sequence. Suppose $f_n \to f$. Since A is continuous, $Af_n \to Af$. On the other hand, by hypothesis, $Af_n \to g$. Hence $Af = g$ and the range of A is all of $\mathbf{H}$. All statements of the theorem have been verified.

A corollary to this theorem is

THEOREM 2-2: *If the bounded self-adjoint transformation A satisfies $A \geq O$, the spectrum lies on the positive real axis:* $\sigma(A) \subset [0, \infty)$.

The previous theorem shows quickly that if λ is a (strictly) positive number, $\lambda > 0$, then $B \geq \lambda I$ implies B^{-1} exists. Write $B = A + \lambda I$. Since $A \geq O$, $A + \lambda I \geq \lambda I$ and therefore $(A + \lambda I)^{-1}$ exists. This means that $-\lambda$ is not in the spectrum of A. Since this is so for each $\lambda > 0$, the set $(-\infty, 0)$ belongs to the resolvent set and the spectrum is a subset of $[0, \infty)$.

We obtain now a result for whose proof we lean heavily on the theory of the last chapter. This is not necessary but it is convenient.

THEOREM 2-3: *For any bounded self-adjoint transformation A,* $\|A^2\| = \|A\|^2$. Furthermore, $\|A\| = r_A$, *where r_A is the spectral radius of A.*

Since for any pair A, B we have $\|AB\| \leq \|A\| \, \|B\|$, it is clear that $\|A^2\| \leq \|A\|^2$. Now let $\epsilon > 0$ be given and choose an element f, $\|f\| = 1$, such that $\|Af\| \geq \|A\| \, \|f\| - \epsilon$. Then $(\|A\| - \epsilon)^2 \leq \|Af\|^2 = (Af, Af) = (A^2f, f) \leq \|A^2f\| \, \|f\| \leq \|A^2\| \, \|f\|^2$. Thus $(\|A\| - \epsilon)^2 \leq \|A^2\|$ and since ϵ is arbitrary, $\|A\|^2 \leq \|A^2\|$. This inequality with the preceding one shows that $\|A\|^2 = \|A^2\|$.[3]

Now, in the last chapter (formula (16)), we proved that $r_A = \lim \|A^n\|^{1/n}$. Thus, since $\|A\| = \|A^2\|^{1/2} = \|A^4\|^{1/4} = \cdots$, we see that $\|A\| = r_A$.

We are now in a position to prove the fundamental theorem of this section.

THEOREM 2-4: *For a self-adjoint transformation A, the following statements are equivalent.*

(a) $\|A\| \leq 1$;
(b) $-I \leq A \leq I$.

[3] The proof assumes that $A \neq O$ and $\epsilon \leq \|A\|$.

Proof: Assume that $\|A\| \leq 1$. Keeping in mind that $(Af, f) \leq \|Af\| \, \|f\| \leq \|A\| \, \|f\|^2$, we have $((I - A)f, f) = (f, f) - (Af, f) \geq \|f\|^2 - \|A\| \, \|f\|^2 \geq 0$, we see that $I - A \geq O$. In a similar manner, we may prove that $I + A \geq O$. Thus (a) implies (b).

Next, assume that $-I \leq A \leq I$. Since $I - A \geq O$, the spectrum of $I - A$ lies in the set $[0, \infty)$, as was proved in theorem 2-2. This means that the spectrum of A lies in the set $(-\infty, 1]$. In a similar manner, we see that since $I + A \geq O$, the spectrum of A lies in the set $[-1, \infty)$. Thus we have that $\sigma(A)$ is a subset of $[-1, 1]$. It follows that $r_A \leq 1$. Since $r_A = \|A\|$ by theorem 2-3, we have that $\|A\| \leq 1$.

Let us discuss briefly the significance of the last theorem. In the first place, suppose that ϵ is some positive number. Then, clearly, the conditions $\|A\| \leq \epsilon$ and $-\epsilon I \leq A \leq \epsilon I$ are equivalent. Suppose now that λ is any real number. Then the conditions $\|A - \lambda I\| \leq \epsilon$ and $(\lambda - \epsilon)I \leq A \leq (\lambda + \epsilon)I$ are equivalent. Now, the significance of the formula (1) (as we have inferred from the discussion in section 6 of Chapter III) is this: For a given self-adjoint transformation A and for any $\epsilon > 0$, it is possible to find a collection $\lambda_1, \lambda_2, \cdots$ of real numbers and mutually orthogonal manifolds $\mathbf{M}_1, \mathbf{M}_2, \cdots$ spanning $\mathbf{H}$ such that on $\mathbf{M}_i$, $\|A - \lambda_i I\| \leq \epsilon$. We may rephrase this by saying that on $\mathbf{M}_i$, $(\lambda_i - \epsilon)I \leq A \leq (\lambda_i + \epsilon)I$. This suggests the form in which we shall establish formula (1). We shall show that if $\cdots \lambda_{-2} \leq \lambda_{-1} \leq \lambda_0 \leq \lambda_1 \leq \lambda_2 \leq \cdots$ is any double sequence, then there exist closed linear manifolds $\mathbf{M}_i$ which are mutually orthogonal and which span the space $\mathbf{H}$ such that on $\mathbf{M}_i$, $\lambda_i I \leq A \leq \lambda_{i+1} I$.

3. The point spectrum

We now consider the point spectrum and the manner in which it can be handled.

DEFINITION 3-1: *If A is any transformation and λ is a scalar we say that λ belongs to the point spectrum in case there exists an*

$f \neq 0$ in the domain of A such that $(A - \lambda I)f = 0$. We shall say that λ belongs to the continuous spectrum if it does not belong to the point spectrum and if the range of $A - \lambda I$ is dense in **H** *but is not all of* **H**.

Suppose A is self-adjoint and that for a given λ, $(A - \lambda I)^{-1}$ does not exist as a bounded, everywhere-defined transformation. Suppose further that λ is not in the point spectrum of A. Then λ belongs to the continuous spectrum of A. For if $(A - \lambda I)f = 0$ implies $f = 0$, then the range of $A - \lambda I$ is dense in **H**. We have gone through this argument before for the case of a bounded A. In the general case, suppose that f is orthogonal to all elements Bg where $B = A - \lambda I$ and $g \in \Delta_B = \Delta_A$. Then $0 = (Bg, f) = (g, 0)$ and since B is self-adjoint (remember that λ is real), $f \in \Delta_B$ and $Bf = 0$. This means that $(A - \lambda I)f = 0$, hence since λ is not in the point spectrum that $f = 0$. Thus the range of $A - \lambda I$ is dense in **H**. If the range were all of **H**, $(A - \lambda I)^{-1}$ would be bounded since it is a closed transformation.

DEFINITION 3-2: *If A is self-adjoint, we say that A has no point spectrum if for each scalar λ, the equation $(A - \lambda I) f = 0$ has only the trivial solution $f = 0$. We say that A has pure point spectrum if the totality of vectors f which are a solution of $(A - \lambda I)f = 0$ for some λ (depending on f) span the space* **H**. *If A has no point spectrum we shall say that A has a purely continuous spectrum.*

Suppose that A has a pure point spectrum. We wish to show that there exists a resolution of the identity E_λ such that formula (1) is valid. If $f \neq 0$ and if $Af = \lambda f$, then f is called a *characteristic vector* and λ is called the *characteristic value* to which f belongs. Another pair of names which do injury to linguistic niceties is *eigenvector* and *eigenvalue.* The characteristic values for a self-adjoint operator are, of course, real. We show now that characteristic vectors belonging to distinct characteristic values are orthogonal. Suppose $\lambda_1 \neq \lambda_2$ and that $Af_1 = \lambda_1 f_1$, $Af_2 = \lambda_2 f_2$. Then $\lambda_1(f_1, f_2) = (Af_1, f_2) = (f_1, Af_2) = \lambda_2(f_1, f_2)$. Hence $(f_1, f_2) = 0$.

Now, suppose λ is a characteristic value. Let $\mathbf{N}_\lambda$ indicate the closed linear manifold of all characteristic vectors corresponding to the characteristic value λ. Introduce in $\mathbf{N}_\lambda$ an orthonormal set $\{q_{\lambda i}\}$ which is complete for $\mathbf{N}_\lambda$. If $\lambda \neq \mu$ and if $\{q_{\mu j}\}$ is the orthonormal set for $\mathbf{N}_\mu$, then $(q_{\lambda i}, q_{\mu j}) = 0$ for each i and j. Hence the union $\{q_{\lambda i}\} \cup \{q_{\mu j}\}$ is a complete orthonormal set for the closed linear manifold $\mathbf{N}_\lambda \oplus \mathbf{N}_\mu$. The statement that "$A$ has a pure point spectrum" is equivalent to the statement that "the union $\bigcup_\lambda \{q_{\lambda i}\}$ over all λ of the orthonormal sets for $\mathbf{N}_\lambda$ is a complete orthonormal set in $\mathbf{H}$."

We now define E_λ for the operator A with pure point spectrum. Let λ be any real number. Let $\mathbf{M}_\lambda$ be the smallest closed linear manifold containing each $\mathbf{N}_\mu$, $\mu < \lambda$: $\mathbf{M}_\lambda = \bigoplus_{\mu<\lambda} \mathbf{N}_\mu$. Let E_λ be the orthogonal projection on $\mathbf{M}_\lambda$. Then E_λ is a resolution of the identity (refer to definition 6-1 of Chapter III). Obviously, $\lambda_1 < \lambda_2$ implies $E_{\lambda_1} \prec E_{\lambda_2}$. The statement that $E_\lambda \to O$ strongly as $\lambda \to -\infty$ and $E_\lambda \to I$ strongly as $\lambda \to \infty$ results from the fact that the set $\bigcup\{q_{\lambda i}\}$ is a complete orthonormal set (the computation is easy and is recommended as a little exercise in the grammar of orthonormal sets).

The following facts may (and should) also be verified. Let $\lambda_1 < \lambda_2$ and consider the smallest linear manifold containing the $\mathbf{N}_\mu$, $\lambda_1 \leq \mu < \lambda_2$. This manifold is precisely the range of the projection $E_{\lambda_2} - E_{\lambda_1}$. On this manifold the transformation A is self-adjoint and bounded and satisfies $\lambda_1 I \leq A < \lambda_2 I$. Referring to the remarks at the end of section 2, we see that we have established formula (1) for the case of a self-adjoint A which has a pure point spectrum.

4. The partition into pure types

The purpose of this section is to show how the problem of a general self-adjoint transformation A can be reduced to the two cases: A has a pure point spectrum; and A has a pure continuous spectrum. To be more precise, we shall demonstrate the following:

THEOREM 4-1: *Let A be a self-adjoint transformation in* $\mathbf{H}$. *Then there exist two closed linear manifolds* $\mathbf{M}_1$ *and* $\mathbf{M}_2$ *such that* $\mathbf{H} = \mathbf{M}_1 \oplus \mathbf{M}_2$, $\mathbf{M}_1 = \mathbf{M}_2^{\perp}$, $\mathbf{M}_2 = \mathbf{M}_1^{\perp}$ *and such that the pair* $\{\mathbf{M}_1, \mathbf{M}_2\}$ *reduces A. Let A_1 and A_2 be the restrictions of A to* $\mathbf{M}_1$ *and* $\mathbf{M}_2$ *respectively. Then A_1 and A_2 are self-adjoint transformations in* $\mathbf{M}_1$ *and* $\mathbf{M}_2$ *respectively. Furthermore, A_1 has a pure point spectrum and A_2 has a pure continuous spectrum.*

The proof of this theorem is only a little longer than its statement and in any case is quite straightforward. There is one preliminary idea and the rest calls for a little checking of a few definitions. The preliminary idea is to let $\mathbf{M}_1$ be the closed linear manifold spanned by all characteristic vectors of A, and to set $\mathbf{M}_2 = \mathbf{M}_1^{\perp}$. We recall that A may be unbounded and hence is defined on a linear manifold Δ which is dense in $\mathbf{H}$. By the restriction A_1 of A to $\mathbf{M}_1$ is meant the intersection Δ_1 of Δ with $\mathbf{M}_1$; similarly for the restriction A_2 of A to $\mathbf{M}_2$, which is defined on $\Delta_2 = \Delta \cap \mathbf{M}_2$.

We shall show first that if $f \in \Delta$, then $f = f_1 + f_2$ where $f_1 \in \Delta_1$ and $f_2 \in \Delta_2$. That is, if P is the orthogonal projection on the manifold $\mathbf{M}_1$, then Δ_1 is precisely the set of vectors of the form Pf where $f \in \Delta$ and Δ_2 is precisely the set of vectors of the form $(I - P)f$ where $f \in \Delta$. Let $\{q_i\}$ be a complete orthonormal set for $\mathbf{M}_1$ whose members are characteristic vectors of A; write $Aq_i = \lambda_i q_i$. Let $f \in \Delta$; let $f^* = \Sigma \alpha_i q_i$ be the Fourier series for f in terms of $\{q_i\}$. We show that $f^* \in \Delta$. Obviously $f^* \in \mathbf{M}_1$ and $f - f^* \in \mathbf{M}_2$. This will prove our contention.

To show that $f^* \in \Delta$, write $\Sigma' \alpha_i q_i$ for any sum involving only a finite number of terms. For such a sum Σ', the operator A^2 is defined and we have

$$(4) \quad (A\,(f - \Sigma'\alpha_i q_i), A(\Sigma'\alpha_i q_i)) = (f - \Sigma'\alpha_i q_i, A^2(\Sigma'\alpha_i q_i)) = 0,$$

since $f - \Sigma'\alpha_i q_i$ is orthogonal to each q_i appearing in $\Sigma'\alpha_i q_i$ and hence is orthogonal to any linear combination of those q_i, such as $A^2\Sigma'\alpha_i q_i = \Sigma'\lambda_i^2\alpha_i q_i$. Therefore

$$(5) \qquad \|Af\|^2 = \|A(f - \Sigma'\alpha_i q_i)\|^2 + \|A(\Sigma'\alpha_i q_i)\|^2.$$

If we allow the number of terms appearing in Σ' to increase, and keeping in mind the orthogonality properties of the q_i, we see that both $\Sigma'\alpha_i q_i$ and $A(\Sigma'\alpha_i q_i)$ converge. Since A is a closed transformation, $f^* \in \Delta$; clearly $f - f^*$ is also in Δ.

We now show that A_1 is self-adjoint in $\mathbf{M}_1$. Let $\{g, h\}$ be any pair of elements in $\mathbf{M}_1$ such that for any $f_1 \in \Delta_1$, $(A_1 f_1, g) = (f_1, h)$. Let $f \in \Delta$ and let $f = f_1 + f_2$ where $f_1 \in \Delta_1$, $f_2 \in \Delta_2$. Then [since $Af_2 \in \mathbf{M}_2$, because $(Af_2, q_i) = (f_2, Aq_i) = (f - f_1, Aq_i) = 0$ for each q_i, and since $Af_1 = A_1 f_1$] $(Af, g) = (Af_1, g) + (Af_2, g) = (Af_1, g) = (f_1, h) = (f_1 + f_2, h) = (f, h)$. Thus $g \in \Delta$ and $Ag = h$ (by the definition of self-adjointness— see section 4 of Chapter III). This means that $g \in \Delta_1$, and $A_1 g = h$. Thus A_1 is self-adjoint on $\mathbf{M}_1$.

The proof that A_2 is self-adjoint on $\mathbf{M}_2$ is similar. It is clear finally that A_1 has a pure point spectrum and that A_2 has a pure continuous spectrum. This results from the construction of the manifold $\mathbf{M}_1$. The theorem is proved.

Having established the fundamental structure formula (1) for the transformation A_1 defined in $\mathbf{M}_1$, it remains to obtain the formula for the transformation A_2 in $\mathbf{M}_2$. Suppose for a moment that this has been done. How, from these results, can we obtain the structure formula for A in $\mathbf{H}$? To this end, let $E_{1\lambda}$ and $E_{2\lambda}$ represent the resolutions of the identity of A_1 and A_2 respectively. Thus $E_{i\lambda}$ is a transformation defined in $\mathbf{M}_i$, $i = 1, 2$. Construct now the transformation $E_\lambda = E_{1\lambda} \oplus E_{2\lambda}$. Then E_λ is the resolution of the identity of A and all the desired results follow. There is only one difficulty: What is the meaning of the symbol "$\oplus$" which joins two operators? We leave to the reader the task of defining it adequately so that the above statements become meaningful and correct. As a guide to the definition, one might remember that a desideratum is the result: $A = A_1 \oplus A_2$.

The above theorem invokes a type of operation of the greatest importance in analysis: the separation in a given situation of the purely discontinuous components from the continuous ones. As an example of the simplest possible situation of this type, we mention the theorem: A monotone increasing function may be expressed uniquely as the sum of a pure function of jumps and a continuous function.

5. The continuous spectrum

We have kept to the end the only matter involving any real difficulty. The digestion of the coming material should cause the reader no trouble if judicious and parallel use is made of the methods developed in Chapter IV. Throughout, the transformation A will be self-adjoint in $\mathbf{H}$ and will have no point spectrum. We shall prove formula (1) in the following form:

THEOREM 5-1: *Let A be a self-adjoint transformation defined in the complex Hilbert space* $\mathbf{H}$. *Let* $\{\lambda_n\}$, $n = 0, \pm 1, \pm 2, \cdots$, *be a double sequence of real numbers such that*

(a) *For every* n, $\lambda_{n+1} > \lambda_n$;

(b) $\lim_{n \to \infty} \lambda_n = \infty; \lim_{n \to -\infty} \lambda_n = -\infty.$

Then there exists a double sequence of closed linear manifolds $\{\mathbf{M}_n\}$, $n = 0, \pm 1, \pm 2, \cdots$, *such that*

(c) $n \neq m$ *implies* $\mathbf{M}_n \perp \mathbf{M}_m$;

(d) *The smallest closed linear manifold containing all the* $\mathbf{M}_n$ *is* $\mathbf{H}$;

(e) A *is defined for each* $f \in \mathbf{M}_n$, $A(\mathbf{M}_n) \subset \mathbf{M}_n$ *and in* $\mathbf{M}_n$, *we have* $\lambda_n I \leq A \leq \lambda_{n+1} I$.

Although this theorem appears first in this section, it will be the last to be proved. Let us make one remark about the relation between it and the resolution of the identity E_λ: This is that the manifold $\mathbf{M}_n$ is the range of the projection $E_{\lambda_{n+1}} - E_{\lambda_n}$. This being the case, it is not difficult to see how to proceed from this theorem to the substantiation of formula (1).

Let us introduce immediately the integral which is the key to the success of the undertaking. Let λ and μ be two real numbers with $\lambda < \mu$. Let C be a simple closed curve in the complex plane which crosses the real axis at the two points λ and μ. Let C be piece-wise smooth (C consists of a finite number of pieces which have a continously turning tangent). C should also be symmetric about the real axis. Finally, C should cut the real axis at λ and μ at an angle which is not zero (for example, C might be a square having opposite vertices at λ and μ). Let m and n represent integers which are strictly positive: $m > 0$, $n > 0$. Consider the integral

$$K_{\lambda\mu}(m, n) = (2\pi i)^{-1} \int_C (\zeta - \lambda)^m (\mu - \zeta)^n R_\zeta \, d\zeta \tag{6}$$

where R_ζ is the resolvent of A.

The integrand is well defined for all points of C with the possible exception of λ and μ. This is due to the fact that R_ζ exists for all non-real complex numbers ζ. Let us examine the integration process in the neighborhood of λ. We know from theorem 4-2 of Chapter III that $\|R_\zeta\| \leq |\eta|^{-1}$ where $\zeta = \xi + i\eta$ is the standard decomposition of ζ into real and imaginary parts. Suppose for a moment that C cuts the real axis at right angles. Then on C, $\zeta = \lambda + i\eta$ and $(\zeta - \lambda)^m = (i\eta)^m$. It is clear now that the integrand is bounded near λ because $m > 0$ (and likewise at μ because $n > 0$) and hence the integral exists. If the curve cuts the real axis non-orthogonally the argument is slightly modified (introduce the sine of the angle). However, it is important that the angle of intersection be strictly positive. Because the curve is symmetric about the real axis, the integral is a bounded self-adjoint transformation. Let us enumerate the properties of $K_{\lambda\mu}(m, n)$ which will interest us.

THEOREM 5-2: *The integral $K_{\lambda\mu}(m, n)$ converges in the uniform topology to a bounded self-adjoint transformation. The value of the integral is not changed if* C *is deformed slightly, providing that the points λ and μ remain fixed under the deformation. Furthermore we have:*

(a) $K_{\lambda\mu}(m, n) \cdot K_{\lambda\mu}(m', n') = K_{\lambda\mu}(m + m', n + n')$.

(b) *If the open intervals (λ, μ) and (λ', μ') have no points in common, then*

$$K_{\lambda\mu}(m, n) \cdot K_{\lambda'\mu'}(m', n') = 0.$$

(c) *The transformation* $A - \lambda I$ *is defined for every vector in the range of* $K_{\lambda\mu}(m, n)$ *and we have*

$$(A - \lambda I)K_{\lambda\mu}(m, n) = K_{\lambda\mu}(m + 1, n);$$

similarly, the transformation $\mu I - A$ *is defined for every vector in the range of* $K_{\lambda\mu}(m, n)$ *and we have*

$$(\mu I - A)K_{\lambda\mu}(m, n) = K_{\lambda\mu}(m, n + 1).$$

(d) *For the elements in the range of* $K_{\lambda\mu}(m, n)$, A *is a bounded self-adjoint transformation and satisfies*

$$\lambda I \leq A \leq \mu I.$$

Figure 3 shows an allowable curve C (symmetric about real axis, piece-wise smooth, and cutting the real axis at a positive angle). It also shows a contemplated deformation of C into a curve C′. Returning to the statement of the theorem, it is clear

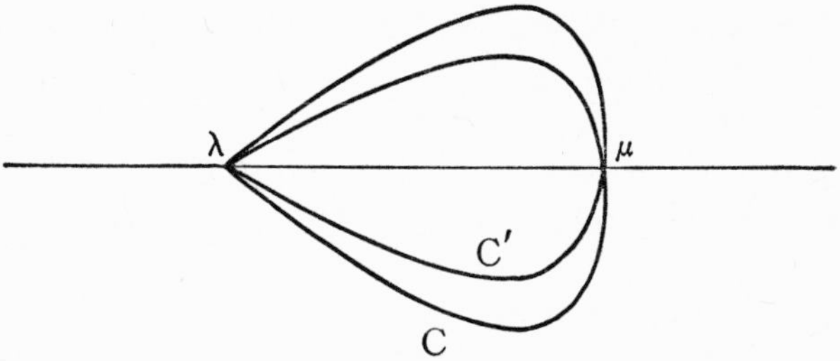

Figure 3.

that the integral value is not changed by this deformation. The argument therefor has been given many times in Chapter IV (see theorem 4-1).

To prove (a) we calculate the integral for $K_{\lambda\mu}(m, n)$ and that for $K_{\lambda\mu}(m', n')$ with two curves C and C′ as shown in figure 3. On the product in (a) we use the functional equation for the resolvent plus the fact that C′ lies interior to C (see the proof of theorem 4-3 or of theorem 7-1 in Chapter IV). The proof of (b) is similar except that here the two curves C and C′ lie exterior to each other and the product of the integrals is zero.

To demonstrate (c), let us begin by observing that A is evidently defined for all elements of the form $(\zeta I - A)^{-1}f$, $f \in \mathbf{H}$. Since $A - \lambda I = (A - \zeta I) + (\zeta - \lambda)I$, the product of $K_{\lambda\mu}(m, n)$ by $A - \lambda I$ gives two integrals, of which one is zero by Cauchy's theorem while the other is equal to $K_{\lambda\mu}(m + 1, n)$. If we examine this argument attentively, we see that use is made of the closure of A. This may be seen in the following manner:

The integral $K_{\lambda\mu}(m, n)$ may be approximated by a finite sum which we shall denote by $\Sigma(m, n)$. If we multiply $\Sigma(m, n)$ by $A - \lambda I$ we obtain an approximating sum $\Sigma(m + 1, n)$ of the integral $K_{\lambda\mu}(m + 1, n)$. We obtain (c) by passing to the limit and using the fact that A is a closed transformation.

In order to demonstrate (d), let us start with the following relations involving inner products:

$$\begin{aligned} &((A - \lambda I)K_{\lambda\mu}(m, n)f,\ K_{\lambda\mu}(m, n)f) \\ (7) \qquad &\qquad = (K_{\lambda\mu}(m + 1, n)f,\ K_{\lambda\mu}(m, n)f) \\ &= (K_{\lambda\mu}(m, n)K_{\lambda\mu}(m + 1, n)f, f) = (K_{\lambda\mu}(2m + 1, 2n)f, f). \end{aligned}$$

We shall show that there exists a bounded self-adjoint transformation $L_{\lambda\mu}(m, n)$ such that

$$(8) \qquad L^2_{\lambda\mu}(2m + 1, 2n) = K_{\lambda\mu}(2m + 1, 2n).$$

This will show that the inner product in (7) is positive (≥ 0) and this fact will complete the demonstration of (d)—at least the part: $\lambda I \leq A$ on the given manifold. To this end let us introduce the integral

$$(9) \qquad L_{\lambda\mu}(m, n) = (2\pi i)^{-1} \int_C (\zeta - \lambda)^{m/2}(\mu - \zeta)^{n/2} R_\zeta \, d\zeta.$$

Notice that the function $(\zeta - \lambda)^{m/2}(\mu - \zeta)^{n/2}$ is analytic in a region consisting of the complex plane from which the closed interval $[\lambda, \mu]$ has been deleted. With the help of arguments now familiar, it may be seen that the integral $L_{\lambda\mu}(m, n)$ exists and represents a bounded self-adjoint transformation. We may also demonstrate by our usual techniques the validity of formula (8). It is only in the case $m = 1$ (or $n = 1$) that we have a new phenomenon, because in this case the transformation $(\zeta - \lambda)^{1/2}R_\zeta$ may have an infinite norm near λ. However, in this case, an argument of the integral calculus resolves the difficulty: We use the fact that $\int_0^1 x^{-1/2}\,dx < \infty$.

This completes the proof of the theorem.

THEOREM 5-3: *Let* $\mathbf{M}_{\lambda\mu}(m, n)$ *be the closure of the range of* $K_{\lambda\mu}(m, n)$. *Let* $\mathbf{N}_{\lambda\mu}(m, n)$ *be the closed linear manifold on which* $K_{\lambda\mu}(m, n) = O$. *Then*

(a) $\mathbf{M}_{\lambda\mu}(m, n)$ *is the orthogonal complement of* $\mathbf{N}_{\lambda\mu}(m, n)$.

(b) $\mathbf{M}_{\lambda\mu}(m, n)$ *is independent of m and n. This manifold will be denoted by* $\mathbf{M}_{\lambda\mu}$.

(c) *If* ν *is a real number such that* $\lambda < \nu < \mu$ *then* $\mathbf{M}_{\lambda\mu} = \mathbf{M}_{\lambda\nu} \oplus \mathbf{M}_{\nu\mu}$, *where the addition is intended in the sense of the orthogonal sum of closed linear manifolds.*

Statement (a) is valid for any self-adjoint transformation and will not be established at this point since we have indicated the method of proof many times. Toward a proof of (b) consider instead $\mathbf{N}_{\lambda\mu}(m, n)$. Since A does not have a point spectrum and since $(A - \lambda I)K_{\lambda\mu}(m, n) = K_{\lambda\mu}(m + 1, n)$, it is clear that $\mathbf{N}_{\lambda\mu}(m + 1, n) = \mathbf{N}_{\lambda\mu}(m, n)$. The proof of (*b*) is now evident.

Toward the proof of (c), let

$T_{\lambda\mu} = (2\pi i)^{-1} \int_{C_{\lambda\mu}} (\zeta - \lambda)(\zeta - \mu)(\zeta - \nu)R_\zeta\, d\zeta$, where for definiteness, $C_{\lambda\mu}$ is a rectangle of height one with sides parallel to the real and imaginary axes, through the points λ and μ. Define similarly $T_{\lambda\nu}$ and $T_{\nu\mu}$. Then it is apparent that $T_{\lambda\mu} = T_{\lambda\nu} + T_{\nu\mu}$ and that $T_{\lambda\nu} \cdot T_{\nu\mu} = O$. A simple calculation shows also that $T_{\lambda\mu} = (\nu I - A)K_{\lambda\mu}(1, 1)$ and hence since A has no point spectrum, the closure of the range of $T_{\lambda\mu}$ is identical with that of $K_{\lambda\mu}(1, 1)$—namely, $\mathbf{M}_{\lambda\mu}$. The conclusion in (c) is now evident.

THEOREM 5-4: Let $\{\lambda_n\}$ *be a double sequence,* $n = 0, \pm 1, \pm 2, \cdots$, *such that* $\lim_{n\to\infty} \lambda_n = \infty$ *and* $\lim_{n\to-\infty} \lambda_n = -\infty$ *and such that* $\lambda_n < \lambda_n + 1$. *Let* $\mathbf{M}_n$ *denote the closure of the range of* $K_{\lambda_n\lambda_{n+1}}(m, m)$. *Then the smallest closed linear manifold containing all the* $\mathbf{M}_n$ *is* $\mathbf{H}$.

Proof: According to (c) of the preceding theorem, it is sufficient to consider the closure of the range $\mathbf{P}_r$ of one single transformation $K_{-r,r}(1, 1)$ as r tends to infinity. In order to demonstrate that $\mathbf{P}_r$ tends to $\mathbf{H}$, we shall show that if f is orthogonal to $\mathbf{P}_r$ for each value of r, then $f = 0$. If we have such an f, then for each $g \in \mathbf{H}$, $0 = (K_{-rr}(1, 1)g, f) = (g, K_{-rr}(1, 1)f)$. We see therefore that $K_{-rr}(1, 1)f = 0$ for each r. If C is the circle $|\zeta| = r$, then since $(2\pi i r^2)^{-1} \int_C (r^2 - \zeta^2)\zeta^{-1}\, d\zeta = 1$,

$$(10) \quad f = (2\pi i r^2)^{-1} \int_C [(r^2 - \zeta^2)\zeta^{-1}I - (r^2 - \zeta^2)R_\zeta]\, d\zeta \cdot f.$$

A simple calculation shows that the integrand is (up to a constant factor) equal to $A(\zeta^2 - r^2)\zeta^{-1}R_\zeta f$. If we put the factor A outside of the integral sign and integrate, we obtain an element which we shall denote by g_r. Thus (10) reads $f = Ag_r$.

Let us carry out a simple evaluation on the norm of the integral. Write, as usual, $\zeta = r(\cos\theta + i\sin\theta)$. Then $\zeta^2 = r^2(\cos 2\theta + i\sin 2\theta)$ and $\zeta^2 - r^2 = r^2(\cos 2\theta - 1 + i\sin 2\theta) = 2r^2(-\sin^2\theta + i\sin\theta\cos\theta)$. We recall that $\|R_\zeta\| \leq |r\sin\theta|^{-1}$. Thus $\|(\zeta^2 - r^2)\cdot R_\zeta\| \leq 2r$. This means that for the element g_r defined by (10) we have, since $|\zeta^{-1}| = r^{-1}$, $\|g_r\| \leq (2\pi r^2)^{-1}r^{-1}\cdot 2r \cdot 2\pi r\|f\| = 2r^{-1}\|f\|$. As $r \to \infty$, $g_r \to 0$. Now $f = Ag_r$ and A is a closed transformation. Therefore, $f = 0$. This shows that the closure of the range $\mathbf{P}_r$ tends to $\mathbf{H}$ as $r \to \infty$. The theorem is proved.

This terminates our task. The reader may now refer to the

statement of theorem 5-1 and see that everything has been proved. The manifolds $\mathbf{M}_n$ are defined in theorem 5-4. This same theorem asserts (d). The proof of (c) begins with the statement (b) of theorem 5-2. Since $K_{\lambda\mu}(m, n) \cdot K_{\lambda'\mu'}(m',n') = O$, the range of one transformation is included in the null space of the other. Now, for any self-adjoint transformation, range and null-space are orthogonal. This terminates the proof of (c). Finally, the proof of (e) is given in theorem 5-2(d).

VI COMMUTATIVE BANACH ALGEBRAS

1. Introduction

The subject of Banach algebras is just one quarter of a century old. Its growth has been substantial.[1] The notion of an *algebra* (slightly sharper than that of a *ring*) involves the multiplication of two elements (whereas in vector spaces we have only addition). It is strange that over a period of 35 years or so, many of the Banach spaces which attracted most attention were also algebras (for example, the space of continuous functions) but their study from this richer point of view was essentially never approached. A rapid examination of Banach's book, published in 1932, seems to show that he multiplies for the first time on p. 153 where he considers the n-th iterate of T: T^n! Students for the doctorate who sometimes feel that everything has already been done should draw valuable conclusions from this circumstance.

The essential first fact for us about Banach algebras is that any such that we treat is isomorphic to an algebra of operators. This is the content of the regular representation theorem. This allows us to develop a complete spectral theory for the elements of the algebra in accordance with Chapter IV. Next comes a classification of all complex Banach algebras which are fields—a class with one element, the field of complex numbers. Then

[1] The early history of Banach algebras is discussed in the author's article, "Normed rings, the first decade," published in the Symposium on Spectral Theory, Stillwater Colloquium, Stillwater, Oklahoma, 1950.

comes the introduction of the notions of ideal, closed ideal, and maximal ideal and the construction of a residue algebra. Finally we consider the class of maximal ideals and its topologization and the representation of the original algebra as an algebra of continuous functions. The introduction of the notion of maximal ideal and with it the entire representation theory is the work of Gelfand. It is the central feature in the theory we are about to expose.[2]

2. Definitions and examples

In this chapter, as was also the case in the last two chapters, we deal exclusively with complex vector spaces. We introduce immediately

DEFINITION 2-1: *A set* R *is called a complex Banach algebra*[3] *if*

(a) R *is a complex vector space.*

(b) *There is defined in* R *the operation of multiplication, written* $f \cdot g$ *or* fg, *satisfying the conditions:* $\lambda(fg) = (\lambda f)g = f(\lambda g)$; $(fg)h = f(gh)$; $f(g + h) = fg + fh$; $(g + h)f = gh + hf$, *for all scalars* λ *and all* $f, g, h \in$ R.

(c) R *is a Banach space whose norm will be indicated by* $\|\cdot\|$.

(d) *For every* $f, g \in$ R, $\|f \cdot g\| \leq \|f\| \, \|g\|$.

[2] The author's early work in Banach algebras was devoted principally to developing a theory of analytic functions. This was completed at the beginning of 1942. Gelfand's very remarkable paper, "Normierte Ringe," was published in Russia in 1941 but due to the emergency occasioned by the Nazi invasion, did not reach this country until the middle of the following year, after the first draft of our own results had been prepared. Much preliminary material was common to both presentations, including the two theorems on algebras which are fields, and sections on the radical (that is, the set of quasi-nilpotents). The rapport between our earlier paper on the reducibility theory of operators and the spectral radius has already been noted in Chapter IV. The link between operator theory and the theory of abstract rings is, as has been stated above, the regular representation theorem.

[3] The early nomenclature for Banach algebras includes such expressions as: *normed rings, normed vector rings,* and *rings of operators.* In Russia, the phrase "normed rings" is still standard.

We shall be interested exclusively in commutative algebras, that is, those which satisfy $f \cdot g = g \cdot f$ for every $f, g \in \mathrm{R}$. Furthermore, we shall assume that R contains an identity element e (also called a unity). The identity e has the property: $ef = fe = f$ for all f. Obviously, it is unique. Note that $e^2 = e$ and, hence, using (d) we have $\|e\| = \|e^2\| \leq \|e\|^2$. We shall assume that R possesses elements which are not zero. It follows that $\|e\| \geq 1$. We shall show shortly that we may assume that $\|e\| = 1$.

Let us give some elementary examples. The field of complex numbers is a Banach algebra. The absolute value serves as norm and satisfies the more stringent relation $|\lambda \cdot \mu| = |\lambda|\,|\mu|$. We shall show that this field is the only complex Banach algebra for which the inequality (d) may be replaced by equality.

The Banach space $\mathbf{C}_{\mathfrak{M}}$ (section 2 of Chapter I) is a Banach algebra if multiplication is defined in the usual way. We recall that $\mathfrak{M}$ is a topological space and $\mathbf{C}_{\mathfrak{M}}$ is the set of all complex valued functions, bounded and continuous on $\mathfrak{M}$. The norm of f is defined by $\|f\| = \sup_{x \in \mathfrak{M}} |f(x)|$. If $\mathfrak{M}$ is compact, we remind the reader that any continuous function is bounded. If the topology in $\mathfrak{M}$ is discrete, then $\mathbf{C}_{\mathfrak{M}}$ consists of all bounded functions.

The Banach space of all complex-valued functions f defined and continuous on the closed disc $|\zeta| \leq 1$ and analytic in the open disc $|\zeta| < 1$ is a Banach algebra providing multiplication is performed in the usual manner. The norm is to be taken as $\|f\| = \sup_{|\zeta| \leq 1} |f(\zeta)|$. If we call the closed disc Δ, then $\mathbf{C}_{\Delta}$ contains functions which are not analytic—for example, the function f for which $f(\zeta) = \bar{\zeta}$—and hence $\mathbf{C}_{\Delta}$ contains the algebra of analytic functions as a proper subalgebra. This fact is very significant.

Let us consider now the algebra of all absolutely convergent Fourier series. The elements of the algebra are the functions f where $f(x) = \sum_{n=-\infty}^{\infty} \alpha_n \exp(inx)$ and where $\sum_{n=-\infty}^{\infty} |\alpha_n| < \infty$. The norm is defined as: $\|f\| = \sum_{n=-\infty}^{\infty} |\alpha_n|$. It is not difficult to show that this totality is indeed a Banach algebra. We do not propose to go through the various computations here, but shall leave them as an exercise to the reader. Of particular interest in this verification are the proofs: that the product of two absolutely convergent Fourier series is one of the same type; that the inequality (d) holds; that the given algebra is complete.

These last examples of Banach algebras arise from domains in analysis which are very central. There are further important types of Banach algebras which are somewhat more complex in their structure and which cannot be considered here.

3. The regular representation

We show in this section that every commutative Banach algebra with an identity element is isomorphic to an algebra of bounded linear operators.

Let a represent a fixed element in R and let x be variable in R. Consider the mapping: $x \rightarrow ax$. Call this mapping T_a. Thus we have $T_a x = ax$. We see that T_a is an operator defined over R and we remind the reader that R is a Banach space. The operator T_a is linear and is bounded; in fact $\|T_a\| \leq \|a\|$. Linearity is trivial and boundedness comes from the relations: $\|T_a x\| = \|ax\| \leq \|a\| \cdot \|x\|$.

The transformation T_a thus belongs to the set of all bounded linear transformations of R into itself, which we have denoted earlier by $\mathfrak{A}(\mathrm{R})$. Let us denote by Φ the mapping: $a \rightarrow T_a$. Thus $\Phi(a) = T_a$. We see that Φ is a mapping of R into $\mathfrak{A}(\mathrm{R})$. We shall show that Φ is an isomorphism.

We have first that for all $x \in \mathrm{R}$, $T_{a+b}\, x = (a + b)x = ax + bx = T_a x + T_b x = (T_a + T_b)x$. Thus $T_{a+b} = T_a + T_b$. Similarly, $T_{ab}\, x = (ab)x = a(bx) = a \cdot T_b x = T_a T_b x$, hence $T_{ab} = T_a T_b$. Next we see that $T_e = I$ since $T_e x = ex = x$. If $T_a = O$, then $T_a e = O$, that is $ae = a = O$. This shows that Φ is an algebraic isomorphism of R into $\mathfrak{A}(\mathrm{R})$.

We now show that the range of Φ is a closed linear manifold in $\mathfrak{A}(\mathrm{R})$. That the manifold is linear is evident. Suppose now that

$\{T_{a_n}\}$ is a Cauchy sequence in the range. Thus for any x in R, $\{T_{a_n}x\}$ is a Cauchy sequence in R. Set $x = e$. Then $\|T_{a_n}e - T_{a_m}e\| = \|a_ne - a_me\| = \|a_n - a_m\| \to 0$. Suppose $a_n \to a$. Then it follows easily that $T_{a_n} \to T_a$ and this proves the closure of the range. This range, being closed in the Banach space $\mathfrak{A}$(R), may itself be considered a Banach space. Thus Φ is a bounded linear transformation (its bound is ≤ 1) of one Banach space onto another. Furthermore Φ^{-1} obviously exists since $T_a = O$ implies $a = 0$. This shows that Φ^{-1} is also bounded (see section 3 of Chapter II). We have therefore proved the following

THEOREM 3-1: *Let* R *be a Banach algebra. Let* Φ *be the transformation of* R *into* $\mathfrak{A}$(R) *defined by* $\Phi(a) = T_a$ *where* $T_ax = ax$. *Then* Φ *is an algebraic and topological isomorphism.*

Note: Topological isomorphism implies that topological properties are faithfully mirrored under Φ. Convergence, openness, are examples of topological properties. The norm is not. We have seen that $\|T_a\| \leq \|a\|$. It is easy to show that $\|a\| = \|T_a\|$ for all $a \in$ R if and only if $\|e\| = 1$.

Let us examine some consequences of this theorem. Suppose $a \in$ R and that a^{-1} exists. Then since $I = T_e = T_{aa^{-1}} = T_aT_{a^{-1}}$, we have: $T_{a^{-1}} = (T_a)^{-1}$. Next suppose that for a given $a \in$ R, there is a transformation S in $\mathfrak{A}$(R) such that $T_aS = I$. Let $Se = b$. Then $e = (T_aS)e = T_ab = ab$ and a^{-1} exists; $a^{-1} = b$. Thus a^{-1} exists in R if and only if T_a has an inverse in $\mathfrak{A}$(R). Let λ be a complex number. We see from the above that $(a - \lambda e)^{-1}$ exists in R if and only if $T_{a-\lambda e} = T_a - \lambda I$ has an inverse in $\mathfrak{A}$(R).

We define the spectrum $\sigma(a)$ of a to consist of those complex numbers λ such that $a - \lambda e$ has no inverse. Similarly, we define the resolvent set $\rho(a)$ to be the complement of $\sigma(a)$. We see that the spectrum of a is identical with the spectrum of T_a. In particular $\sigma(a)$ is not empty. The isomorphism theorem allows us to carry over to the study of R the entire mechanism of the Cauchy theory of Chapter IV. This is so because the method of contour integration involves the notion of uniform convergence of operators, a concept which is invariant under the isomorphic mapping Φ or its inverse.

Under the circumstances we shall hereafter assume that the identity e of R satisfies $\|e\| = 1$. In this case Φ is an isometry as well as an isomorphism and both metrically and algebraically, the set of elements a and the set of transformations T_a are indistinguishable.

4. Reducibility and idempotents

An idempotent in R is an element j such that $j^2 = j$. Proper idempotents are idempotents distinct from 0 and e. The spectrum of a proper idempotent consists precisely of the numbers 0 and 1. (Computation: If $\lambda \neq 0$, $\lambda \neq 1$, then the inverse of $\lambda e - j$ is $\lambda^{-1}(\lambda - 1)^{-1}j + \lambda^{-1}e$, as is evident by direct multiplication. If $aj = e$, then since $j(e - j) = 0$, $e - j = (e - j)aj = 0$; if $b(e - j) = e$, then $j = jb(e - j) = 0$. This proves that for a proper idempotent j, $\sigma(j) = \{0, 1\}$.) We now state a necessary and sufficient condition for the existence in R of proper idempotents.

THEOREM 4-1: *There exists a proper idempotent in* R *if and only if there exists an element f whose spectrum is not a connected set.*

Suppose j is a proper idempotent. Then $\sigma(j) = \{0, 1\}$ which is not a connected set. Suppose now that $f \in$ R is such that $\sigma(f)$ is not connected. Let C be a simple closed curve (rectifiable) lying in the resolvent set of f such that both the interior and the exterior of C contain points of $\sigma(f)$. Define: $j = (2\pi i)^{-1} \int_C (\zeta e - f)^{-1}\, d\zeta$. Then (according to section 4 of Chapter IV) j is an idempotent, $j^2 = j$, and $j \neq 0$, $j \neq e$ since the spectrum of f is not concentrated either in C or outside C. Thus j is a proper idempotent. This proves the theorem.

Suppose that j is a proper idempotent. Suppose $a \in$ R; write $a = a_1 + a_2$ where $a_1 = ja$ and $a_2 = (e - j)a$. This gives a decomposition of R into a direct sum: $R = R_1 \oplus R_2$. Note that for any a, b in R, $a_1b_2 = 0$ since $a_1b_2 = ja(e - j)b = (j - j^2)ab = 0$. That is, R_1 and R_2 annihilate each other. Notice further that in R_1, j is an identity (and $e - j$ is an identity in R_2).

Now, suppose that $R = R_1 \oplus R_2$ is a proper direct sum decomposition of R into two algebras R_1 and R_2 and suppose R_1 and R_2 annihilate each other. Suppose that in this decomposition $e = e_1 + e_2$ where $e_i \in R_i$. Then $e = e^2 = e_1^2 + e_2^2 = e_1 + e_2$ since $e_1e_2 = 0$; since the sum decomposition is direct, we have $e_1^2 = e_1$ and $e_2^2 = e_2$; that is, e_1 and e_2 are idempotents. Suppose further that in this decomposition, for an arbitrary $a \in R$, $a = a_1 + a_2$. Then $e_1a = e_1a_1 + e_1a_2 = e_1a_1 \in R_1$ and similarly $e_2a \in R_2$. Since $a = ea = e_1a + e_2a$, we see that $e_1a = a_1$ and $e_2a = a_2$. This means that the decomposition: $R = R_1 \oplus R_2$ is generated by idempotents. We have thus proved that each proper decomposition of R into the direct sum of two subalgebras which annihilate each other is generated by a proper idempotent in the manner indicated. And conversely, each proper idempotent gives a decomposition of R. In case R has a decomposition of the indicated type, we say that it is reducible. Thus the question of establishing reducibility is identical with that of finding idempotents.

5. Algebras which are fields

The task of this section is to determine which (complex) Banach algebras are fields. The answer is simple: Only the complex number system is such.

This theorem was given by Mazur in 1938 and was established independently later by Gelfand and the author. A second theorem with a similar history asserts that if R is a Banach algebra such that $\|fg\| = \|f\|\,\|g\|$ for all pairs f, g then R is the set of complex numbers. The former theorem is particularly important to the Gelfand representation theory. Its proof is trivial once one has established the cardinal fact that the spectrum of an element is not empty (see theorem 4-2 of Chapter IV).

THEOREM 5-1: *If the complex Banach algebra* R *is a field, then* R *is isomorphic to the field of complex numbers.*

Proof: An algebra is a field providing every non-zero element f is regular (has an inverse). Let $f \in$ R. Then the spectrum of f is not empty. Suppose $\lambda \in \sigma(f)$. Then $f - \lambda e$ is singular. Since R is a field, $f - \lambda e = 0$, that is, $f = \lambda e$. This proves the theorem. It should be noted that the result is valid also in case the commutative hypothesis for R is not invoked. To carry out the proof one should go over some aspects of our discussion of the regular representation.

THEOREM 5-2: *Let* R *be a Banach algebra such that* $\|fg\| = \|f\|\,\|g\|$ *for each pair* f, g *in* R. *Then* R *is isomorphic to the field of complex numbers.*

(Note first that $e = e^2$ implies $\|e\| = 1$.) Suppose f is any regular element: $f \cdot f^{-1} = e$. The relation $(\zeta e - f)^{-1} = -\zeta^{-1}f^{-1} \cdot (\zeta^{-1}e - f^{-1})^{-1}$, valid for $\zeta \neq 0, \zeta^{-1} \neq 0$, implies that the spectrum of f^{-1} consists of the reciprocals of the spectrum of f. Clearly, $1 \leq r_f \cdot r_{f^{-1}}$ and the equality holds only if $\sigma(f)$ is concentrated on the circle $|\zeta| = r_f$. Also $r_f \leq \|f\|$. By hypothesis $\|f\|\,\|f^{-1}\| = 1$. Thus $r_f = \|f\|$ and $\sigma(f)$ lies on the circle $|\zeta| = r_f$.

If α is some complex number, the spectrum of $f - \alpha e$ is obtained from that of f by a translation by the factor α. If we make α small, then $f - \alpha e$ is regular and the above argument applies. This shows easily that the spectrum of f consists of one point only. We have assumed at the start that f was regular, but the conclusion clearly holds for all elements in R (using the translation argument).

Let f be arbitrary and suppose λ is the unique point in its spectrum. We show that $f - \lambda e = 0$ and this will conclude the proof of the theorem. Let $\{\lambda_n\}$ be a sequence of numbers such that $\lambda_n \to \lambda$, $\lambda_n \neq \lambda$. Then $f - \lambda_n e \to f - \lambda e$; $\sigma(f - \lambda_n e) = \{\lambda - \lambda_n\}$; and since $f - \lambda_n e$ is regular, $\|f - \lambda_n e\| = |\lambda - \lambda_n|$. It follows that $\|f - \lambda e\| = 0$, hence $f - \lambda e = 0$.

6. Ideals

We introduce now the notion of ideal in a Banach algebra R. The reader should classify any ideal coming to his attention under three headings: general, closed, and maximal. We shall concentrate most of our attention on maximal ideals (which turn out to be closed). We shall also establish theorems of importance for closed ideals. We shall have little interest in general ideals. The principal definition follows.

DEFINITION 6-1: *An ideal* I *in a Banach algebra* R *is a subset which is a linear manifold in* R *and such that* $f \in \mathrm{I}$ *and* $x \in \mathrm{R}$ *implies* $xf \in \mathrm{I}$.

The definition implies that $f \pm g$ and αf are in I whenever f, g are in I and α is any complex number. We remind the reader that since all algebras are commutative we need not speak of right or left ideals. It is clear that R itself is an ideal. We shall say that R is an *improper* ideal; all other ideals will be *proper*. Since R possesses an identity, we see that if I is a proper ideal and $f \in \mathrm{I}$, then f is singular. Suppose, to the contrary, that f^{-1} exists (in R). Then $f^{-1}f = e$ belongs to I by definition. If $g \in \mathrm{R}$, then $ge = g \in \mathrm{I}$, once more by definition. Hence $\mathrm{R} = \mathrm{I}$. This contradicts the propriety of I, hence f is singular.

An ideal I is said to be a *closed* ideal providing that I is a closed subset of R. If $f \in \mathrm{R}$, the set I of all elements of the form xf, $x \in \mathrm{R}$, is an ideal. It is the *principal* ideal generated by f. In particular, this ideal is proper if and only if f is singular. Thus if $f \in \mathrm{R}$ and $\lambda \in \sigma(f)$, the principal ideal generated by $f - \lambda e$ is a proper ideal.

The intersection of an arbitrary family of ideals is an ideal. The intersection of an arbitrary family of closed ideals is a closed ideal.

Let us show briefly that the closure of a proper ideal is a proper ideal.

THEOREM 6-1: *Let* I *be a proper ideal. Let* $\bar{\mathrm{I}}$ *denote the closure* (*in the norm topology*) *of* I. *Then* $\bar{\mathrm{I}}$ *is a proper ideal.*

Let f and g be in $\bar{\mathrm{I}}$. Choose sequences $\{f_n\}$, $\{g_n\}$ such that $f_n \to f$, $g_n \to g$, and f_n, $g_n \in \mathrm{I}$. Then $f_n + g_n \to f + g$ and since $f_n + g_n \in \mathrm{I}$, $f + g \in \bar{\mathrm{I}}$. Similarly, $xf_n \to xf$ for $x \in \mathrm{R}$ and since $xf_n \in \mathrm{I}$, $xf \in \bar{\mathrm{I}}$.

It remains to show that $\bar{\mathrm{I}}$ is proper. This results from the fact that the set of singular elements of a Banach algebra is closed—a fact which we show immediately below. Applied to the present situation, we see that the closure of any set of singular elements consists of singular elements. Hence $\bar{\mathrm{I}}$ is proper.

THEOREM 6-2: *The set of regular elements of a Banach algebra is open. The set of singular elements is closed.*

Suppose f is regular. Then all elements g satisfying $\|f - g\| < \|f^{-1}\|^{-1}$ are also regular. This follows the fact that $g = f(e - f^{-1}(f - g))$ and the standard expansion such as is given in theorem 1-1 of Chapter IV. Hence the set of regular elements is open.

A proper ideal is said to be *maximal* providing that it is not contained in any strictly larger proper ideal. It may be seen that any maximal ideal is closed. For if I is maximal, $\mathrm{I} \subset \bar{\mathrm{I}}$ and $\bar{\mathrm{I}}$ is proper. Hence $\mathrm{I} = \bar{\mathrm{I}}$.

We give an example of a maximal ideal. Let $\mathfrak{M}$ be a compact space and consider the algebra $\mathrm{C}_{\mathfrak{M}}$ of all functions continuous on $\mathfrak{M}$ defined earlier. Let $\xi \in \mathfrak{M}$ and let $\mathrm{I} = \{f : f \in \mathrm{C}_{\mathfrak{M}}; f(\xi) = 0\}$—that is, I is the set of all functions which vanish at ξ. I is clearly an ideal. We show that I is maximal. Specifically, we show that if $g \notin \mathrm{I}$, then the smallest ideal containing I and g contains e and is therefore R. Suppose $g(\xi) = 1$. Then setting $h = g - e$ we see that $h(\xi) = 0$ hence $h \in \mathrm{I}$. Thus $e = g - h$ is in this ideal.

The existence of maximal ideals in suitable profusion is of the greatest importance to the sequel. The necessary result is given in

THEOREM 6-3: *Let* I *be any proper ideal. Then there exists a maximal ideal* K *containing* I. *In particular, if f is singular in* R, *then there exists a maximal ideal containing f.*

The proof is straightforward. Let T be the totality of proper ideals which contain I. Then a partial ordering may be introduced into T based on the notion of ordinary set inclusion. Let C represent any chain in T, that is, any totally ordered subset of T. Then the union of all the ideals in C is an ideal; it is proper; and it majorizes each ideal of C in the sense of the partial ordering of T. Applying Zorn's lemma we see that T has a maximal element.

If $f \in \mathbf{R}$ and f is singular, the principal ideal generated by f is proper. By applying the previous paragraph, f may be embedded in a maximal ideal. More generally, if g is arbitrary in R and if λ is in the spectrum of g then $g - \lambda e$ is singular, hence, is to be found in some maximal ideal.

The totality of maximal ideals suitably topologized plays a very important role in the study of R. For example in the ring $\mathbf{C}_{\mathfrak{M}}$ where $\mathfrak{M}$ is a compact space, this topologized totality is (isomorphic to) $\mathfrak{M}$. Note that we have shown a few lines earlier that every point ξ in $\mathfrak{M}$ gives rise to a maximal ideal. The proof that there are no further maximal ideals in this special case will be given forthwith.

Suppose $\mathbf{K}$ is a maximal ideal in $\mathbf{C}_{\mathfrak{M}}$ which does not consist of all functions f vanishing on some fixed point ξ_0 in $\mathfrak{M}$. Thus for every $\xi \in \mathfrak{M}$, there exists an $f \in \mathbf{K}$ $(f = f_\xi)$ such that $f(\xi) \neq 0$. By the compactness of $\mathfrak{M}$ and the continuity of the functions f, we see that there exist functions $f_1, \cdots, f_n$ in $\mathbf{K}$ such that the function $g = f_1\bar{f}_1 + \cdots + f_n\bar{f}_n$ does not vanish at any point of $\mathfrak{M}$. Clearly $g \in \mathbf{K}$; also g^{-1} exists (in R) since $\mathfrak{M}$ is compact. Thus $gg^{-1} = e \in \mathbf{K}$ and $\mathbf{K}$ is not proper. This contradiction shows that the map $\xi \rightarrow \{f : f(\xi) = 0\}$ is one-to-one and onto from $\mathfrak{M}$ to the set of maximal ideals in $\mathbf{C}_{\mathfrak{M}}$.

7. Quotient algebras

If R is an algebra and I is an ideal in R, one may construct the quotient-algebra R/I. We shall show that if R is a Banach algebra and if I is a closed ideal, then it is possible to introduce a norm in R/I in a "natural" manner so that R/I is a Banach algebra (hence complete). This construction is particularly important in case I is a maximal ideal (hence closed). Here, R/I is a field and since it is also a Banach algebra, it is the field of complex numbers by theorem 5-1. This fact is central in the representation theory.

Suppose R is an algebra and I is an ideal. Let $f \in$ R. Denote by $\{I + f\}$ the set of all elements of the form $x + f$ where $x \in$ I. For given elements f and g it is obvious that $\{I + f\} \cap \{I + g\} = \varnothing$ or $\{I + f\} = \{I + g\}$. The class of sets $\{I + f\}$ is denoted by R/I. In R/I one may introduce the operations of scalar multiplication, addition and multiplication, written respectively $\alpha\{I + f\}$, $\{I + f\} + \{I + g\}$, and $\{I + f\} \cdot \{I + g\}$. These three operations are performed by choosing arbitrary representatives and proceeding as in R. For example, if $x_1, x_2 \in$ I, then $(x_1 + f)(x_2 + g) \in$ R, say $(x_1 + f)(x_2 + g) = h$. Then by definition $\{I + f\}\{I + g\} = \{I + h\}$. The reader should prove that this product is independent of elements x_1, x_2 chosen at the outset. The sum and product by scalars is defined similarly. It is not difficult to show that with respect to these three operations R/I is an algebra (hence it satisfies a brace of conditions concerning commutativity, associativity, distributivity, and existence of an identity). The zero in R/I is the coset $\{I + 0\} =$ I. The identity in R/I is the coset $\{I + e\}$ where e is the identity of R. Notice that R/I contains as a subset (a set isomorphic to) the field of complex numbers. This is the subset of all cosets of the form $\{I + \lambda e\}$ where λ is an arbitrary complex number.

Suppose that I is maximal. Let f be such that $f \notin$ I. Then $\{I + f\} \neq$ I, that is, $\{I + f\}$ is not the zero of R/I. The set of all elements $x + yf$ where $x \in$ I and $y \in$ R is an ideal containing I as a proper subset (it contains I and also f). Hence this ideal is R since I is maximal. Thus there exist elements $x_0 \in$ I and $g \in$ R such that $x_0 + gf = e$. This means that $\{I + f\} \cdot \{I + g\} = \{I + e\}$. Thus $\{I + f\}^{-1}$ exists in R/I. Since each non-zero element in R/I is regular, R/I is a field.

Consider an ideal I in R and the quotient algebra R/I. Write $R' = R/I$ and $f' = \{I + f\}$. Suppose $\mathbf{K}'$ is an ideal in R', say, $\mathbf{K}' = \{f'_\alpha\}$, where α runs over some set of indices. Set $\mathbf{K} = \bigcup_\alpha \{I + f_\alpha\}$. Then **K** is an ideal in R which contains I. Conversely, let K be an ideal in R which contains I. Let K′ be the set of all elements f'_β where $f_\beta \in$ K and $f'_\beta = \{\text{I} + f_\beta\}$. Then K′ is an ideal in R′ = R/I. As an application, let R′ = R/I be a field. Since a field has no proper ideals except $\{0'\}$, then I has no proper ideal extensions in R. Thus I is maximal.

Thus R/I is a field if and only if I is maximal.

We come now to the proof of the principal theorem of this section.

THEOREM 7-1: *Let* I *be a closed ideal in the Banach algebra* R. *If* $f' = \{\text{I} + f\}$ *is an element of* R′ = R/I, *define*

$$\|f'\| = \inf_{x \in \text{I}} \|x + f\|. \tag{1}$$

Then $\|f'\|$ *is a norm in* R′. *With respect to this norm* R′ *is complete and satisfies* $\|f'g'\| \leq \|f'\| \, \|g'\|$; *thus* R′ *is a Banach algebra.*

Clearly, $\|f'\| \geq 0$. Also, since $0 \in$ I, $\inf_{x \in \text{I}} \|x\| = 0$. Hence, $\|0'\| = 0$. To prove that $\|f'\| = 0$ implies $f' = 0'$ we use the closure of I. Writing $f' = \{\text{I} + f\}$, we must show that $\{\text{I} + f\} = \text{I}$, that is, that $f \in$ I. Let $\{x_n\}$ be a sequence of elements in I such that $\|x_n + f\| \to 0$. Then $\{x_n\}$ is a Cauchy sequence since $\|x_n - x_m\| \leq \|x_n + f\| + \|x_m + f\| \to 0$. Let $x_n \to x$. Since I is closed, $x \in$ I. Obviously, $\|x + f\| = 0$, $x + f = 0$, $-f \in$ I, hence finally $f \in$ I.

We shall not bother to show that $\|\alpha f'\| = |\alpha| \, \|f'\|$. Let us consider the triangle inequality: $\|f' + g'\| \leq \|f'\| + \|g'\|$. Choose an $\epsilon > 0$. Find elements $x_1, x_2 \in$ I such that $\|x_1 + f\| - \epsilon \leq \|f'\|$, $\|x_2 + g\| - \epsilon \leq \|g'\|$. Then $\|f' + g'\| = \inf_{x \in \text{I}} \|x + f + g\| \leq \|x_1 + x_2 + f + g\| \leq \|x_1 + f\| + \|x_2 + f\| \leq \|f'\| + \|g'\| + 2\epsilon$. Since ϵ is arbitrary we have the desired result. This shows that R/I is a normed space.

We now show that $\|f'g'\| \leq \|f'\| \, \|g'\|$. For $\epsilon > 0$, find x_1 and x_2 as in the preceding paragraph. Note that $f'g' = \{\text{I} + fg\}$ and that $x_1x_2 + x_1g + x_2f \in$ I. Then $\|f'g'\| = \inf_{x \in \text{I}} \|x + fg\| \leq$

$\|x_1x_2 + x_1g + x_2f + fg\| = \|(x_1 + f)(x_2 + g)\| \leq \|x_1 + f\| \cdot \|x_2 + g\| \leq (\|f'\| + \epsilon)(\|g'\| + \epsilon)$. This leads to the desired result.

It remains to show that R/I is complete in the indicated norm. Consider a Cauchy sequence in R'. The Cauchy sequence consists of cosets $\{I + f_n\} = f'_n$. The statement that $\{f'_n\}$ is a Cauchy sequence means that $\|f'_n - f'_m\| \to 0$. Note that $f'_n - f'_m = \{I + f_n\} - \{I + f_m\} = \{I + f_n - f_m\}$. If $\{f_n\}$ is a Cauchy sequence in R, write $f_n \to f$. Then $\{I + f_n\} \to \{I + f\} = f'$. This comes from the fact that $\|f' - f'_n\| \leq \|f - f_n\| \to 0$ and hence $f'_n \to f'$. This proves completeness in this case. In general, of course, $\{f_n\}$ is not a Cauchy sequence in R. The problem is then to find elements x_n in I such that $\{x_n + f_n\}$ is a Cauchy sequence. Notice that $\{I + x_n + f_n\} = \{I + f_n\} = f'_n$.

As a first step, we replace the sequence $\{f'_n\}$ by a subsequence $\{f'_{n_k}\}$ with the property: $\|f'_{n_1} - f'_{n_2}\| + \|f'_{n_2} - f'_{n_3}\| + \cdots < 1$. This can be done as follows: Choose n_1 so that $r, s \geq n_1$ imply $\|f'_r - f'_s\| < 2^{-1}$; choose $n_2 > n_1$ so that $r, s \geq n_2$ imply $\|f'_r - f'_s\| < 2^{-2}$; and so on.

Next, for $k = 1, 2, \cdots$, choose x_k in I as follows: $x_1 = 0$; x_2 so that $\|f'_{n_2} - f'_{n_1}\| \geq \|(x_2 + f_{n_2}) - (x_1 + f_{n_1})\| - 2^{-1}$; x_3 so that $\|f'_{n_3} - f'_{n_2}\| \geq \|(x_3 + f_{n_3}) - (x_2 + f_{n_2})\| - 2^{-2}$; and so on. Then the sequence $\{x_k + f_{n_k}\}$ is a Cauchy sequence in R. For, if we write $g_k = x_k + f_{n_k}$, then $\sum_{k=1}^{\infty} \|g_{k+1} - g_k\| \leq \sum_{k=1}^{\infty} \|f'_{n_{k+1}} - f'_{n_k}\| + 1 < 2$. Now, if $r < s$, then $\|g_r - g_s\| \leq \|g_r - g_{r+1}\| + \cdots + \|g_{s-1} - g_s\|$. Since $\sum_{k=1}^{\infty} \|g_{k+1} - g_k\|$ converges, $\|g_r - g_s\| \to 0$ as $r, s \to \infty$ and hence $\{g_k\}$ is a Cauchy sequence.

Let $\{g_k\} = \{x_k + f_{n_k}\}$ converge to f. Then, as we have seen above, $f' = \{I + f\}$ is the limit of the Cauchy sequence $\{f'_{n_k}\}$. (Details: note first that $f' - f'_{n_k} = \{I + f\} - \{I + f_{n_k}\} = \{I + f - (x_k + f_{n_k})\}$, and next that $\|f' - f'_{n_k}\| \leq \|f - (x_k + f_{n_k})\| \to 0$.)

Finally, f' is the limit of the Cauchy sequence $\{f'_n\}$ with which we started. This is an immediate consequence of the relation: $\|f' - f'_r\| \leq \|f' - f'_{n_k}\| + \|f'_{n_k} - f'_r\| \to 0$ as $r, k \to \infty$. This terminates the proof of completeness of R/I. Theorem 7-1 is therefore proved.

THEOREM 7-2: *Let* I *be a maximal ideal in* R. *The quotient ring* $R' = R/I$ *is isomorphic to the field of complex numbers. If* $f \in R$, *there exists one and only one complex number* λ*—we write* $\lambda = f(I)$*—such that* $\{I + f\} = \{I + \lambda e\}$. *Equivalently expressed,* $f \equiv \lambda e \pmod{I}$.

Some remarks: It may strike the reader that the notation $I(f)$ would be superior to $f(I)$. The fact is that both notations have suggestive power. The notation $f \equiv \lambda e \pmod{I}$—read "$f$ is congruent to λe modulo I"—means that $f - \lambda e$ is in I.

Now to the proof. Since I is maximal, R/I is a field. Furthermore for any ideal I, R/I contains the cosets $\{I + \lambda e\}$; hence R/I is an extension of the complex numbers. Since I is maximal, it is closed. Hence by the preceding theorem, R/I is a Banach algebra. By theorem 5-1, R/I is the field of complex numbers.

Let us look at the matter a little more closely. Let $f \in R$; write $f' = \{I + f\}$. The proof of theorem 5-1 shows that $f' = \lambda e'$ for some λ. Thus $\{I + f\} = \{I + \lambda e\}$. This states that $f - \lambda e \in I$. Our argument thus shows that R/I is an improper extension of the complex numbers. That is, the cosets of the form $\{I + \lambda e\}$ exhaust R/I.

8. Homomorphisms and maximal ideals

The word "homomorphism" in this section will mean "homomorphism of R onto the complex numbers." We shall show that the notion of homomorphism is equivalent to that of maximal ideal. More precisely, the kernel of each homomorphism is a maximal ideal and each maximal ideal is the kernel of some homomorphism. The totality of homomorphisms is given a "weak" topology in which it becomes a compact space: the *structure space* of R (also known as the *space of maximal ideals*).

A homomorphism $f \to Ff$ is a mapping "preserving" algebraic and topological properties. More precisely

DEFINITION 8-1: *A mapping F from the algebra* R *onto the complex number is called a homomorphism providing that*

(a) $F(\alpha f + \beta g) = \alpha Ff + \beta Fg$;

(b) $F(f \cdot g) = Ff \cdot Fg$;

(c) *F is continuous.*

Note first that we exclude the mapping $f \to Ff = 0$ by requiring that the range of F be all complex numbers. Next, since R is a Banach space, conditions (a) and (c) state that F is a continuous linear functional. According to section 3 of Chapter I, F is a bounded linear functional. Condition (b) states that F is multiplicative. Thus a homomorphism is a multiplicative linear functional and conversely. The proof of the theorem which follows shows that condition (c) is redundant.

THEOREM 8-1: *If F is a homomorphism of* R *onto the complex numbers, then* $\|F\| = 1$.

Let f be chosen so that $Ff \neq 0$. Then $Ff = F(ef) = Fe \cdot Ff$. Thus $Fe = 1$ and hence $1 = |Fe| \leq \|F\| \, \|e\| = \|F\|$.

Next for an arbitrary f, let $Ff = \lambda$. Then $F(f - \lambda e) = Ff - \lambda Fe = \lambda - \lambda = 0$. We conclude that $f - \lambda e$ is singular. For if $g \in \mathrm{R}$ is such that $g(f - \lambda e) = e$ then $1 = Fe = Fg \cdot F(f - \lambda e) = Fg \cdot 0 = 0$. Since $f - \lambda e$ is singular, λ is in the spectrum of f. It follows that $|\lambda| \leq \|f\|$. Hence $|Ff| \leq \|f\|$ or $\|F\| \leq 1$. The theorem now follows.

THEOREM 8-2: *Let F be a homomorphism of* R *onto the complex numbers and let* I *be the kernel of F, that is,* $\mathrm{I} = \{f : Ff = 0\}$. *Then* I *is a maximal ideal.*

Conversely, let I *be a maximal ideal and let F be the mapping* $Ff = f'$ *where* $f' = \{\mathrm{I} + f\}$ *of* R *onto* R/I. *Then F is a homomorphism of* R *onto the complex numbers and the kernel of F is* I.

Proof: Let F be a homomorphism and let I be its kernel. Let $f, g \in \mathrm{I}$ and $x \in \mathrm{R}$; thus $Ff = 0$ and $Fg = 0$. Now, $F(\alpha f + \beta g) =$

$\alpha Ff + \beta Fg = 0$ hence $\alpha f + \beta g \in \mathbf{I}$. Also $F(xf) = Fx \cdot Ff = Fx \cdot 0 = 0$, hence $xf \in \mathbf{I}$. It follows that $\mathbf{I}$ is an ideal. Note that $\mathbf{I} \neq \mathbf{R}$ since $F \neq O$.

For a given $f \in \mathbf{R}$, let $f' = \{\mathbf{I} + f\}$. If $Ff = \lambda$ then $\{\mathbf{I} + \lambda e\} = \{\mathbf{I} + f\}$ since $F(f - \lambda e) = 0$ and hence $f - \lambda e \in \mathbf{I}$. It follows that the map $f \rightarrow Ff$ is precisely the map $f \rightarrow f' \in \mathbf{R}/\mathbf{I}$. Thus $\mathbf{R}/\mathbf{I}$ is the field of complex numbers and $\mathbf{I}$ is maximal.

Conversely, let $\mathbf{I}$ be a maximal ideal in $\mathbf{R}$. Then $\mathbf{R}' = \mathbf{R}/\mathbf{I}$ is the field of complex numbers, that is, for each $f \in \mathbf{R}$, there is a unique complex number λ such that $\{\mathbf{I} + f\} = \{\mathbf{I} + \lambda e\}$. Define F by $Ff = \lambda$. If $g \in \mathbf{R}$ and $\{\mathbf{I} + g\} = \{\mathbf{I} + \mu e\}$, then one sees easily that $\{\mathbf{I} + f + g\} = \{\mathbf{I} + (\lambda + \mu)e\}$ and $\{\mathbf{I} + fg\} = \{\mathbf{I} + \lambda\mu e\}$. Thus $F(f + g) = Ff + Fg$ and $F(fg) = Ff \cdot Fg$. This completes the proof, since, as we have seen, a multiplicative linear functional is necessarily continuous.

The theorem states that the notions of homomorphism and maximal ideal are equivalent. Cutting linguistic corners we shall frequently consider them identical. For example, each homomorphism is a point on the unit sphere of $\mathbf{R}^*$, the space conjugate to $\mathbf{R}$. Thus the totality of homomorphisms is a subset of this unit sphere. We shall say instead that the set of maximal ideals is a subset of the sphere.

Another important contribution of the theorem regards the plentitude of homomorphisms: There are as many as there are maximal ideals. On the other hand, we have seen earlier that every ideal may be extended to a maximal ideal. In particular, if $f \in \mathbf{R}$ and $\lambda \in \sigma(f)$, then $f - \lambda e$ is singular. Hence there exists a homomorphism F such that $F(f - \lambda e) = 0$, that is, such that $Ff = \lambda$. Conversely, if $Ff = \lambda$ then $F(f - \lambda e) = 0$ and $f - \lambda e$ is singular. Thus the spectrum of f consists precisely of the set of values $\{Ff\}$ where F ranges over all homomorphisms.

From now on let us designate maximal ideals by $\mathbf{M}$, and let the set of all maximal ideals be designated by $\mathfrak{M}$. For a given $\mathbf{M} \in \mathfrak{M}$ and $f \in \mathbf{R}$, we have already defined the expression $f(\mathbf{M})$ (see theorem 7-2). We repeat that $f(\mathbf{M}) = \lambda$ where λ is the unique complex number such that $\{\mathbf{M} + f\} = \{\mathbf{M} + \lambda e\}$. For a given f, the mapping $M \to f(M)$ is a function with domain $\mathfrak{M}$ and range in the complex numbers. We shall denote this function by $f(\ )$. Thus we have that $f(\ )$ maps $\mathfrak{M}$ into the complex numbers. Note that we have disclosed another mapping here: $f \to f(\ )$. This latter mapping is defined over R and has its range in the set of all complex-valued functions defined on $\mathfrak{M}$. We shall study both these mappings extensively.

We shall introduce a topology in $\mathfrak{M}$ with the help of the functions $f(\ )$. The topology is defined by giving a basis of open neighborhoods for each $M_0 \in \mathfrak{M}$. For a given $\epsilon > 0$ and $f_1, \cdots, f_n$ in R let

$$(2)\quad \begin{aligned} &U(M_0; f_1, \cdots, f_n; \epsilon) \\ &\quad = \{M : M \in \mathfrak{M}, |f_i(M) - f_i(M_0)| < \epsilon, i = 1, \cdots, n\}. \end{aligned}$$

The sets in (2) which we shall call $U(M_0)$ for short have the following properties: (1) $M_0 \in U(M_0)$; (2) the intersection of two of these sets contains a third; (3) if $M \in U(M_0)$, there exists a $V(M)$ such that $M_0 \notin V(M)$, $V(M) \subset U(M_0)$.

The desired topology in $\mathfrak{M}$ is obtained by taking as its open sets arbitrary unions of sets of type $U(M_0; f_1, \cdots, f_n; \epsilon)$, the variables varying in all possible ways. It may be verified in a straightforward manner that this gives a topology over $\mathfrak{M}$. The topology is separated: given M_1 and M_2 in $\mathfrak{M}$, there exist neighborhoods $U(M_1)$ and $U(M_2)$ such that $U(M_1) \cap U(M_2) = \varnothing$.

It is clear that the topology here defined is the weakest in which all the functions $f(\ )$ are continuous. Let us refer for a moment to the definition of the weak* topology in section 7 of Chapter I. This is a topology over B^*, the adjoint of a Banach space B. It is the weakest topology in which are continuous the functions defined by: $F \to Ff$ where F varies over B^* and f is fixed in B. Now, in the present case, $\mathfrak{M}$ is a subset of (the unit sphere of) R^*. If we consider the weak* topology over R^* and then consider the topology it induces on $\mathfrak{M}$, we have *precisely* the topology defined by the neighborhoods in (2). Using another expression, the topology we have defined on $\mathfrak{M}$ is the *trace* on $\mathfrak{M}$ of the weak* topology defined in $\mathbf{R}^*$.

We have proved in theorem 7-1 of Chapter I that in the weak* topology the unit ball of $\mathbf{R}^*$ is compact. We shall now prove

THEOREM 8-3: *The space $\mathfrak{M}$ of maximal ideals on* R *is compact in the weak* topology introduced above.*

Since the unit ball Σ of $\mathbf{R}^*$ is compact in the weak* topology, it suffices to prove that $\mathfrak{M}$ is a closed subset of Σ. Let F_0 be a limit point in Σ of the set $\mathfrak{M}$ in the given topology (the reader may prefer to write the elements of $\mathfrak{M}$ as homomorphisms instead of maximal ideals). It is easy to show that F_0 itself is a homomorphism. In fact, $F_0 \in \Sigma$ hence F_0 is a bounded linear functional and $\|F_0\| \leq 1$. Given $\epsilon > 0$ and the elements f, g and fg in R, find a homomorphism F (hence in $\mathfrak{M}$) such that $|Ff - F_0 f| < \epsilon$, $|Fg - F_0 g| < \epsilon$, and $|F(fg) - F_0(fg)| < \epsilon$. (Notice that we write Ff instead of $f(\mathbf{M})$—where $\mathbf{M}$ is the maximal ideal corresponding to F.) Using the fact that $F(fg) = Ff \cdot Fg$, we write $F_0(fg) - F_0 f F_0 g = (F_0(fg) - F(fg)) + (F(fg) - FfFg) + Fg(Ff - F_0 f) + F_0 f(Fg - F_0 g)$. Taking absolute values we see that $|F_0 fg - F_0 f F_0 g| \leq \epsilon(1 + \|g\| + \|f\|)$. Since ϵ is arbitrary, we have $F_0 fg = F_0 f F_0 g$. Obviously, $F_0 e = 1$ hence $F_0 \neq O$. Thus F_0 is a homomorphism, hence $F_0 \in \mathfrak{M}$ and $\mathfrak{M}$ is closed.

Let us consider an example. Let $\mathcal{S}$ be a compact space. Consider the set $\mathbf{C}_{\mathcal{S}}$ of all complex-valued continuous functions defined on $\mathcal{S}$. If x_0 is a point of $\mathcal{S}$ and f is an arbitrary function in $\mathbf{C}_{\mathcal{S}}$ then the mapping $f \to f(x_0)$ is a homomorphism on $\mathbf{C}_{\mathcal{S}}$. The kernel, hence maximal ideal, of the homomorphism is the set of all f such that $f(x_0) = 0$. We have seen at the end of section 6 that there are no maximal ideals other than these. Thus the maximal ideals of $\mathbf{C}_{\mathcal{S}}$ can be identified in a natural way with the points of $\mathcal{S}$. In addition, it may be seen that the topology on the set of maximal ideals is identical with the topology on $\mathcal{S}$. Indeed, since the functions in $\mathbf{C}_{\mathcal{S}}$ are all continuous in the topology of $\mathcal{S}$, and since the topology on the space of maximal ideals is the weakest making all these functions continuous, it is clear that the latter topology is coarser than the former. The converse proposition follows from the fact that if $\mathfrak{A}$ is an open set in a compact space $\mathfrak{S}$, and $x_0 \in \mathfrak{A}$, there exists a function f in $\mathbf{C}_{\mathfrak{S}}$ which vanishes on the complement of $\mathfrak{A}$ and such that $f(x_0) = 1$.

9. The radical

In this section we consider the notions of radical, nil-potent, quasi-nilpotent, semi-simple algebra. The principal result gives several characterizations of the radical. We begin with

DEFINITION 9-1: *The radical of a (commutative) Banach algebra* **R** *is the intersection of all maximal ideals.*

Let **K** denote the radical. Then since the intersection of closed ideals is a closed ideal, **K** is a closed ideal.

DEFINITION 9-2: *If the radical of a Banach algebra* **R** *is the ideal* $\{0\}$, **R** *is called semi-simple (also without radical).*

THEOREM 9-1: *If* **K** *is the radical of the Banach algebra* **R**, *then the algebra* **R**/**K** *is semi-simple.*

If **M** is a maximal ideal in **R**, then the cosets of **M** modulo **K** form a maximal ideal **M**$'$ of **R**$'$ = **R**/**K**. Conversely, if **M**$'$ is a maximal ideal in **R**$'$ = **R**/**K**, then the union of the **K**-cosets in **M**$'$ is a maximal ideal **M** in **R**. This shows that the intersection of all maximal ideals in **R**$'$ contains only the coset **K** = $0'$. Hence **R**$'$ is semi-simple.

The following theorem characterizes the radical.

THEOREM 9-2: *The following statements are equivalent for an element f in a Banach algebra* **R**:

(a) *f belongs to the radical;*

(b) *the spectrum of f consists of the one point* $\lambda = 0$;

(c) *for every complex number μ, the sequence* $\{(\mu f)^n\}$ *converges to zero.*

Proof: (a) $\Rightarrow$ (b). Suppose f belongs to the radical. Suppose λ belongs to the spectrum of f. Then $f - \lambda e$ is singular and hence belongs to some maximal ideal **M** (theorem 6-3). However, $f \in \mathbf{M}$ hence $\lambda e \in \mathbf{M}$. As a consequence, $\lambda = 0$.

(b) $\Rightarrow$ (c). Suppose the spectrum of f consists of the unique point $\lambda = 0$. For any complex μ, the spectrum of μf also consists of the unique point $\lambda = 0$. By section 5 of Chapter IV, $e = \lim_{n \to \infty} (e - \mu^n f^n)^{-1}$ and hence $\mu^n f^n \to 0$.

(c) $\Rightarrow$ (a). The hypothesis $(\mu f)^n \to 0$ implies that the spectrum of μf lies in the circle: $|\zeta| \leq 1$. Since this is true for all μ, the spectrum of f is the unique point $\zeta = 0$. Now, let **M** be a maximal ideal and suppose $f(\mathbf{M}) = \lambda$. Then $f - \lambda e \in \mathbf{M}$ and λ belongs to the spectrum of f. Hence $\lambda = 0$ and $f \in \mathbf{M}$. This establishes (a).

An element f such that for some integer n, $f^n = 0$ is called a *nilpotent.* An element f such for all μ, $(\mu f)^n \to 0$ is called a *quasi-nilpotent.* Thus, the radical is precisely the set of quasi-nilpotents. Obviously, any nilpotent is a quasi-nilpotent. Nilpotents are well known in the theory of matrices.

Consider once more the algebra $\mathbf{C}_{\mathcal{S}}$ where $\mathcal{S}$ is a compact topological space. We have seen that the maximal ideal space of $\mathbf{C}_{\mathcal{S}}$ is (isomorphic to) the space $\mathcal{S}$. Suppose f belongs to each maximal ideal. Then for each $x_0 \in \mathcal{S}$, $f(x_0) = 0$. This means that $f = 0$, and hence $\mathbf{C}_{\mathcal{S}}$ is semi-simple.

Let us give an example of a Banach algebra with radical. For a fixed integer $n > 1$, consider the set of all $n \times n$ matrices of complex numbers (α_{ij}). These form an algebra with respect to the usual matrix operations. Note that the algebra is not commutative. The quantity $\left(\sum_{ij} |\alpha_{ij}|^2\right)^{1/2}$ is a norm over this algebra and with respect to this norm, the algebra is complete. Also convergence according to the norm is equivalent to entry-wise convergence.

Consider now the subalgebra of the above consisting of the matrices which have as entries: zero under the main diagonal; a constant λ along the main diagonal; a constant α_1 on the diagonal above the main diagonal; a constant α_2 on the diagonal above the previous; and so on. This algebra is commutative. It has a unique maximal ideal consisting of all matrices in the algebra with zero entries along the main diagonal. All these matrices belong to the radical. Each of these matrices is a nilpotent.

10. The representation theory

A representation of a mathematical structure X is a second (presumably better known type of) structure Y which "reproduces" (usually with less detail) the phenomena of the first structure. The "reproduction" is given by a mapping process from X to Y which is a homomorphism. If the homomorphism is an isomorphism, then the image set of X in Y reproduces *faithfully* the structure of X.

The representation theory we shall develop can be described briefly as follows: Let $\mathbf{R}$ be any (commutative) Banach algebra and let $\mathfrak{M}$ be the compact topological space of its maximal ideals. Let $\mathbf{C}_{\mathfrak{M}}$ be, as usual, the Banach algebra of all complex continuous functions defined on $\mathfrak{M}$ with the customary norm. Then there exists a natural homomorphism of $\mathbf{R}$ into $\mathbf{C}_{\mathfrak{M}}$. The homomorphism is both algebraic and topological. In case $\mathbf{R}$ has no radical, the mapping is an isomorphism for algebraic operations. It is not in general a topological isomorphism (commonly referred to as a homeomorphism). The question as to whether it is an isomorphism onto $\mathbf{C}_{\mathfrak{M}}$ is considerably more complicated and has received answers from many angles. We do not propose to pursue this question.

Let $\mathbf{M}$ be a fixed maximal ideal of $\mathfrak{M}$ and let $f, g, f + g, f \cdot g$ be in $\mathbf{R}$. We have seen that the coset $\{\mathbf{M} + f\}$ contains a unique element of the form λe where λ is complex. Thus $\{\mathbf{M} + f\} = \{\mathbf{M} + \lambda e\}$. We have seen that the mapping $f \rightarrow \lambda$ is a homomorphism of $\mathbf{R}$ onto the complex numbers. Thus if $f \rightarrow \lambda$ and $g \rightarrow \mu$ then $f + g \rightarrow \lambda + \mu$ and $f \cdot g \rightarrow \lambda \cdot \mu$

Now let f be fixed in $\mathbf{R}$ and let $\mathbf{M}$ vary in $\mathfrak{M}$. Then the number

λ depends on f and on $\mathbf{M}$ and is indicated by the symbol $f(\mathbf{M})$. Thus each f gives rise to a mapping of $\mathfrak{M}$ into the complex numbers which we have denoted by $f(\ \ )$. Since the topology on $\mathfrak{M}$ is the weak* topology, the functions $f(\ \ )$ are continuous on $\mathfrak{M}$. Since $\mathfrak{M}$ is compact, $f(\ \ )$ is bounded on $\mathfrak{M}$. The set of values assumed by $f(\ \ )$ is the set $\{\lambda : f(\mathbf{M}) = \lambda,\ \mathbf{M} \in \mathfrak{M}\}$. We have seen that this set of values is precisely the spectrum of f. Thus $\sigma(f) = \{\lambda : f(\mathbf{M}) = \lambda,\ \mathbf{M} \in \mathfrak{M}\}$. This shows that $\sup_{\mathbf{M}\in\mathfrak{M}} |f(\mathbf{M})| = r_f$. Since this supremum is the norm of $f(\ \ )$ in the space $\mathbf{C}_{\mathfrak{M}}$, we have $\|f(\ \ )\| = r_f \leq \|f\|$.

THEOREM 10-1: *Let Ω denote the map of* R *into* $\mathbf{C}_{\mathfrak{M}}: f \to f(\ \ )$. *Then Ω is an algebraic and topological homomorphism. That is,*

(a) $\Omega(\alpha f) = \alpha\Omega f$;
(b) $\Omega(f + g) = \Omega f + \Omega g$;
(c) $\Omega(f \cdot g) = \Omega f \cdot \Omega g$.

If $f_n \to f$, then $\Omega f_n \to \Omega f$.

The proof is essentially contained in the preceding paragraph. We start with the fact that two complex-valued functions ϕ and ψ defined on a space $\mathcal{S}$, are equal if and only if $\phi(x) = \psi(x)$ for each $x \in \mathcal{S}$. To prove (b) for instance, note that at the point $\mathbf{M} \in \mathfrak{M}$, $\Omega(f + g) = f(\mathbf{M}) + g(\mathbf{M})$. Similarly, $\Omega f + \Omega g$ at the point $\mathbf{M}$ has the value $f(\mathbf{M}) + g(\mathbf{M})$. A like argument establishes (c). Suppose now that $f_n \to f$, that is $\|f - f_n\| \to 0$. Since $\|f(\ \ ) - f_n(\ \ )\| \leq \|f - f_n\|$, we have that $f_n(\ \ ) \to f(\ \ )$.

THEOREM 10-2: *The mapping $\Omega: f \to f(\ \ )$ of the Banach algebra* R *into the algebra* $\mathbf{C}_{\mathfrak{M}}$ *is an algebraic isomorphism if and only if* R *is semi-simple.*

Clearly, Ω is an isomorphism if and only if its kernel (the set of elements f such that $f(\ \ ) = 0$) consists of the single element $f = 0$. Suppose now that $f(\ \ ) = 0$, that is, that $f(\mathbf{M}) = 0$ for all $\mathbf{M} \in \mathfrak{M}$. Thus $f \in \mathbf{M}$ for each $\mathbf{M}$ hence f is in the radical of R. If R is semi-simple, $f = 0$. If $f = 0$ is the only element such that $f(\ \ ) = 0$, then the radical contains only 0 and **R** is semi-simple.

Note that, in general, the mapping Ω is not a topological isomorphism. Although the map Ω is continuous, its inverse Ω^{-1} need not be so. This is due to the fact that $\|f(\ )\| \leq \|f\|$ and thus the topology in $\mathbf{C}_{\mathfrak{M}}$ is coarser than the topology in **R**.

11. Illustrative examples and applications

Let **H** be a Hilbert space which for the sake of simplicity we shall assume to be separable and let $\{q_n\}$ be a complete orthonormal set in **H**. Let T be any bounded linear transformation of **H** into itself and suppose that $\|T\| < 1$. Write $S = I - T$ and note that S^{-1} exists (theorem 1-1 of Chapter IV). Let $p_n = Sq_n$. Then the set $\{p_n\}$ is a basis in **H**—a complete *heterogonal* set. Each element $f \in \mathbf{H}$ can be expanded into a series, $f = \sum_{n=1}^{\infty} \alpha_n p_n$, which is unique. The proof is trivial. Start with $g = S^{-1}f$ and suppose $g = \sum_{n=1}^{\infty} \alpha_n q_n$ is the expansion of g according to the set $\{q_n\}$. Then $f = Sg = \sum_{n=1}^{\infty} \alpha_n S q_n = \sum_{n=1}^{\infty} \alpha_n p_n$.

An application of the above yields the result of Paley and Wiener concerning Fourier series expansions. In $\mathbf{L}^2_{[0,1]}$, the sequence $\{q_n\}$ where $q_n(x) = \exp\ (2\pi i n x)$ is orthonormal and complete. It can be shown (by a delicate calculation that we shall not reproduce here) that there exists a constant $\mathrm{k} > 0$, such that $|\lambda_n - n| < \mathrm{k}$, $n = 1, 2, \cdots$, implies the existence of transformations T and S as in the previous paragraph such that $p_n(x) = \exp\ (2\pi i \lambda_n x)$. This yields expansions of any function in $\mathbf{L}^2_{[0,1]}$ in terms of non-harmonic Fourier series.

For a given integer $n > 1$, consider the set of $n \times n$ complex matrices. This set is, as we have seen, a non-commutative Banach algebra (the norm can be introduced as indicated in section 9).

The dimension of this set considered as a vector space is n^2. Let a represent a fixed matrix and let $R = R(a)$ represent the smallest ring containing a and the unit matrix e. Then R is commutative; also, the dimension of R is finite and equal to or less than n^2. Let the dimension be r. Thus the elements $e = a^0$, $a^1, \cdots, a^r$ are linearly dependent; that is, there exists a polynomial p of degree $\leq r$ such that $p(a) = 0$. In other words, every matrix satisfies a polynomial equation.

Let $p(\lambda)$ be any fixed polynomial such that $p(a) = 0$. Let $\lambda_1 \in \sigma(a)$. Then $p(\lambda_1) = 0$. Thus the spectrum of a consists of a finite number of values $\lambda_1, \cdots, \lambda_s$ all of which are roots of $p(\lambda)$. Furthermore it is clear that we may assume that $p(\lambda)$ has no other roots. [For example, suppose $p(\lambda) = (\lambda - \mu)q(\lambda)$ where $\mu \notin \sigma(a)$. Then $p(a) = 0$ implies $q(a) = 0$ since $(a - \mu e)$ is regular.] Let C_t be a small circle in the complex plane about λ_t, $t = 1, \cdots, s$, and let $j_t = (2\pi i)^{-1} \int_{C_t} (\zeta e - a)^{-1} \, d\zeta$. Then j_t is an idempotent and R is a direct sum of subalgebras: $R = R_1 \oplus \cdots \oplus R_s$ where $R_t = R \cdot j_t$.

If $\mathbf{M}$ is a maximal ideal in R, then $j_t(\mathbf{M}) = 1$ if and only if $a(\mathbf{M}) = \lambda_t$. Otherwise, $j_t(\mathbf{M}) = 0$. Thus $(a - \lambda_t)j_t$ has the single point 0 in its spectrum. It follows from the preceding paragraph that for some integer r_t, which we shall assume minimal, we have $(aj_t - \lambda_t j_t)^{r_t} = 0$.

For any polynomial $p(\lambda)$, $p(a) = p(a)j_1 + \cdots + p(a)j_s = p(aj_1) + \cdots + p(aj_s)$. Also $p(a) = 0$ if and only if $p(aj_t) = 0$ for each t. Now, let $q(\lambda) = (\lambda - \lambda_1)^{r_1} \cdots (\lambda - \lambda_s)^{r_s}$. Then $q(aj_t) = 0$ for each t, hence $q(a) = 0$. Also, $q(\lambda)$ is of minimal degree with respect to this property.

Let R be an algebra and consider a fixed element a in R. Let $R(a)$ be the closure of the polynomials in a. Then since addition and multiplications are continuous, $R(a)$ is a Banach algebra. We proceed to determine the maximal ideal space $\mathfrak{M}$ in $R(a)$. If $b \in R(a)$ there exists a sequence of polynomials in a, $\{p_n(a)\}$

such that $p_n(a) \to b$. Let $\lambda \in \sigma(a)$. Then $p_n(a) - p_n(\lambda)e$ is in the principal ideal $(a - \lambda e)$ and since $|p_n(\lambda) - p_m(\lambda)| \leq \|p_n(a) - p_m(a)\|$, it is easy to see that $\{p_n(\lambda)\}$ converges, say, $p_n(\lambda) \to \mu$; also $b - \mu e$ is in the closure of the ideal $(a - \lambda e)$. This means that each coset of the closed ideal contains a scalar of the form μe and hence the closed ideal is maximal. We see therefore that each $\lambda \in \sigma(a)$ gives rise to a maximal ideal which is the closure of the principal ideal $(a - \lambda e)$. It is easy to see that the converse is true: Each maximal ideal arises from some $\lambda \in \sigma(a)$. For if M is maximal, then $a \equiv \lambda e$ (mod M) for some λ and hence $\lambda \in \sigma(a)$. The reader should convince himself that the topology in $\mathfrak{M}$ is the same as that induced on the spectrum of a by the usual metric topology of the complex plane.

We have seen that in any algebra R, the spectrum of $a \in$ R satisfies $\sigma(a) = \{\lambda : \lambda = a(\mathrm{M}),\ \mathrm{M} \in \mathfrak{M}\}$. Suppose now that $f(\zeta)$ is analytic in a region containing $\sigma(a)$ and that C is a simple curve in this region containing $\sigma(a)$ in its interior. Then we have defined $f(a) = (2\pi i)^{-1} \int_{\mathrm{C}} f(\zeta)(\zeta e - a)^{-1}\, d\zeta$. Since this integral is approximated in the norm topology by sums of the type $(2\pi i)^{-1} \sum_{i=1}^{n} f(\zeta_i)(\zeta_i e - a)^{-1}\, \Delta\zeta_i$ as indicated in Chapter IV, we have for any $\mathrm{M} \in \mathfrak{M}$, $f(a)(\mathrm{M})$ is approximated by sums $(2\pi i)^{-1} \sum_{i=1}^{n} f(\zeta_i)(\zeta_i - \lambda)^{-1}\, \Delta\zeta_i$ where $\lambda = a(\mathrm{M})$ is in $\sigma(a)$. Since C contains λ in its interior, $f(a)(\mathrm{M}) = f(\lambda)$. Thus $\sigma(f(a)) = \{\mu : \mu = f(\lambda),\ \lambda \in \sigma(a)\}$. This is the *spectral mapping theorem* due to Dunford.

Let R_1 and R_2 be Banach algebras for which $\mathrm{R}_1 \subset \mathrm{R}_2$. Let $a \in \mathrm{R}_1$. Let $\sigma_1(a)$ and $\sigma_2(a)$ represent the spectrum of a in R_1 and R_2 respectively. Obviously $\sigma_1(a) \supset \sigma_2(a)$. However, as an example later in this section shows, the inclusion may be proper. This raises the problem of removing the spectral singularities of an element by extending the algebra in which the element is embedded.

The set $\sigma_1(a)$ may have interior points and it does have frontier points. We shall show that if λ belongs to the frontier of $\sigma_1(a)$ then it belongs to $\sigma_2(a)$. Thus frontier points in the spectrum are *permanent singularities.*[4] Suppose for simplicity that $\lambda = 0$ belongs to the frontier of $\sigma_1(a)$. Then every neighborhood of a contains non-singular elements. Thus there exists a sequence $\{a_n\}$ for which $a_n \in \mathrm{R}_1$, a_n^{-1} exists, $a_n \to a$. Suppose that $\|a_n^{-1}\| \leq$ k, $n = 1, 2, \cdots$. Then $\|aa_n^{-1} - e\| = \|(a - a_n)a_n^{-1}\| \leq \mathrm{k}\|a - a_n\| \to 0$ and hence for large n, aa_n^{-1} is not singular and thus a is not singular. This shows that $\|a_n^{-1}\| \to \infty$. Writing $b_n = a_n^{-1}/\|a_n^{-1}\|$, we have $b_n \in \mathrm{R}_1$, $\|b_n\| = 1$, $ab_n = (a - a_n)b_n + a_nb_n \to 0$. This shows that a is singular in R_2 for if a^{-1} existed in R_2 we would have $b_n = a^{-1}ab_n \to 0$, which is absurd.

Let A be a bounded self-adjoint transformation in Hilbert space. Let $\mathfrak{Q} = \{\zeta : (\zeta I - A)^{-1} \in \mathfrak{A}(\mathbf{H})\}$, where $\mathfrak{A}(\mathbf{H})$ represents the algebra of all bounded transformations of $\mathbf{H}$ into $\mathbf{H}$. Thus, if E_λ is the resolution of the identity of A, $\mathfrak{Q}$ is the complement of the set of real numbers λ in the neighborhood of which E_λ is not constant; in particular, $\mathfrak{Q}$ contains all complex non-real numbers. Let R be the Banach algebra generated by the polynomials in A and in the operators $(\zeta I - A)^{-1}$, $\zeta \in \mathfrak{Q}$. Let $\mathrm{R}(A)$ be the Banach algebra generated by the polynomials in A. Clearly $\mathrm{R}(A) \subset \mathrm{R}$. We shall show that $\mathrm{R}(A) = \mathrm{R}$.

Let σ denote the set of real numbers λ in the neighborhood of which E_λ is not constant. Thus σ is the spectrum of the element A in R. Let $\sigma(A)$ denote the spectrum of A in $\mathrm{R}(A)$. Since $\mathrm{R} \supset \mathrm{R}(A)$, $\sigma \subset \sigma(A)$. By the preceding discussion, all frontier points of $\sigma(A)$ are permanent spectral singularities. Obviously, therefore, $\sigma(A)$ cannot contain non-real numbers. Similarly, $\sigma(A)$

[4] Due to G. Shilov and the author.

cannot contain real numbers which are not in σ. Hence $\sigma = \sigma(A)$. This means that if $\zeta \in Q$, $(\zeta I - A)^{-1} \in R(A)$ and therefore $R(A) = R$.

If $p(\lambda)$ indicates a polynomial, we have $p(A) = \int p(\lambda)\, dE_\lambda$ where the integration process is that described in section 6 of Chapter III for the special case $p(\lambda) = \lambda$. The discussion of that section shows readily (due to the orthogonality properties of the resolution of the identity) that $\|p(A)\| = \sup_{\lambda \in \sigma(A)} |p(\lambda)|$. We have seen in an earlier paragraph that the space $\mathfrak{M}$ of maximal ideals in $R(A)$ is (isomorphic to) the set $\sigma(A)$. If $f(\lambda)$ represents any function continuous on $\sigma(A)$—we may as well assume that $f(\lambda)$ is defined and continuous in a closed interval containing $\sigma(A)$—then $f(\lambda)$ may be approximated uniformly by a sequence $\{p_n(\lambda)\}$ of polynomials. Thus the sequence $\{p_n(A)\}$ converges to a limit in $R(A)$ which will be denoted by $f(A)$. It is clear that $\|f(A)\| = \sup_{\lambda \in \sigma(A)} |f(\lambda)|$. This argument shows that $R(A)$ is isomorphic (metrically and algebraically) to the ring of all continuous functions on $\sigma(A) = \mathfrak{M}$. We may write $R(A) = \mathbf{C}_{\mathfrak{M}}$. The content of these paragraphs is frequently referred to as the *spectral theorem* (sophisticated form). The content of formula (1) of Chapter V is the spectral theorem in an earlier version.

Let **H** be an infinite-dimensional Hilbert space and let U be a unitary transformation in **H** whose spectrum consists precisely of all points ζ on the unit circle $|\zeta| = 1$. Let $R(U)$ be the ring of all polynomials in U and their limits in the uniform topology. Then, writing $\sigma(U)$ to denote the spectrum of U in the ring $R(U)$, it is clear that $\sigma(U)$ contains the unit circle $|\zeta| = 1$. We shall show immediately that $\sigma(U)$ is the unit disc $|\zeta| \leq 1$. (This gives an example of a transformation whose spectrum diminishes as the ring is extended; if R denotes the ring of all polynomials in U *and* U^{-1} then the spectrum of U in R is only the unit circle.) If $|\zeta| > 1$, then $(\zeta I - U)^{-1} = \zeta^{-1}I + \zeta^{-2}U + \zeta^{-3}U^2 + \cdots$ and hence exists in $R(U)$. Hence $\sigma(U) \subset \{\zeta : |\zeta| \leq 1\}$.

Let $p(\lambda)$ be any polynomial and let E_ζ be the complex resolution of the identity associated to U (see section 8 of Chapter III). Then (since $\|U\| = \|U^{-1}\| = 1$) it is easy to see that E_ζ is concentrated on the circle $|\zeta| = 1$ (that is, is constant at other points); and also that $p(U) = \int p(\zeta)\, dE_\zeta$. Furthermore, due to the orthogonality properties of E_ζ, it is clear that $\|p(U)\| = \sup_{|\zeta|=1} |p(\zeta)|$. If $\{p_n(\zeta)\}$ is a sequence of polynomials, $\{p_n(U)\}$ converges in $\mathrm{R}(U)$ if and only if $\{p_n(\zeta)\}$ is uniformly convergent on $|\zeta| = 1$. By the maximum modulus principle, $\{p_n(\zeta)\}$ converges uniformly to a function $f(\zeta)$ analytic in $|\zeta| < 1$ and continuous in $|\zeta| \leq 1$. The operator to which $\{p_n(U)\}$ converges will be denoted by $f(U)$.

Let λ satisfy $|\lambda| < 1$. Then no sequence $\{p_n(\zeta)\}$ converges uniformly on $|\zeta| = 1$ to the function $f(\zeta) = (\lambda - \zeta)^{-1}$. Thus $\mathrm{R}(U)$ does not contain the transformation $(\lambda I - U)^{-1}$. This implies that $\sigma(U)$ consists of the disc $|\zeta| \leq 1$. Since $\mathrm{R}(U)$ is generated by U, its maximal ideal space $\mathfrak{M} = \sigma(U)$. Note that $\mathrm{R}(U)$ is a proper subalgebra of $\mathbf{C}_{\mathfrak{M}}$.

Let R be any algebra without radical and let $a \in \mathrm{R}$. Let $0 \neq f(\zeta) = \alpha_0 + \alpha_1\zeta + \alpha_2\zeta^2 + \cdots$ be a power series which contains the disc $|\zeta| \leq \|a\|$ in the interior of its circle of convergence. Suppose $f(a) = \alpha_0 e + \alpha_1 a + \alpha_2 a^2 + \cdots = 0$. We show that $\sigma(a)$ consists of n points $\lambda_1, \cdots, \lambda_n$ and that $p(a) = 0$ where $p(\zeta) = (\zeta - \lambda_1) \cdots (\zeta - \lambda_n)$.

Let $\lambda \in \sigma(a)$. Then $|\lambda| \leq \|a\|$ and $f(\lambda)$ is in the spectrum of $f(a) = 0$, that is, $f(\lambda) = 0$. Since $f(\zeta) \neq 0$ identically for all ζ, the number of zeros of $f(\zeta)$ inside $|\zeta| \leq \|a\|$ is finite, and we see that $\sigma(a)$ consists of a finite number of distinct points $\lambda_1, \cdots, \lambda_n$. Let $j_k = (2\pi i)^{-1} \int_{C_k} (\zeta e - a)^{-1}\, d\zeta$ where C_k is a small circle around λ_k. Then j_k is an idempotent and $e = j_1 + \cdots + j_n$. Write $a = aj_1 + \cdots + aj_n$. Then the spectrum of $aj_k - \lambda_k j_k$ consists of the one point $\lambda = 0$ and since R is without radical, $aj_k - \lambda_k j_k = 0$. It is now easy to see that $p(a) = 0$ where $p(\zeta) = (\zeta - \lambda_1) \cdots (\zeta - \lambda_n)$.

An application: Given $f(\zeta) = \exp(2\pi i\zeta) - 1$ and suppose that for some $a \in R$, $f(a) = 0$. Then λ_k is an integer r_k and we have $a = r_1 j_1 + \cdots + r_n j_n$, that is, a is a sum (and difference) of idempotents, with possible repetitions. Conversely, any such sum is a period of the exponential function, that is, for such a sum a, we have $\exp(2\pi i a) = e$. Suppose now that we drop the restriction that R be without radical. Then the above argument shows that $a = r_1 j_1 + \cdots + r_n j_n + b$ where b is in the radical of R. We see quickly, using the multiplicative properties of the exponential function, that $\exp(2\pi i b) - e = 0$, that is, that $0 = 2\pi i b + (2\pi i b)^2/2! + \cdots = 2\pi i b(e + (2\pi i b)/2! + \cdots)$ $= 2\pi i b\,(e + c)$, say. Clearly c is in the radical of R; thus $e + c$ is regular and this gives $b = 0$. Thus in all (commutative) rings, the periods of the exponential function are precisely the finite sums and differences of the idempotents of R. This shows that R is irreducible if and only if the exponential function is simply periodic.[5]

Let R be the totality of absolutely convergent power series. Thus

$$f \in \mathrm{R} \quad \text{where} \quad f(\zeta) = \alpha_0 + \alpha_1\zeta + \alpha_2\zeta^2 + \cdots \quad \text{if} \quad \sum_{n=0}^{\infty} |\alpha_n| < \infty.$$

Introduce addition and multiplication in the usual way and write $\|f\| = \sum_{n=0}^{\infty} |\alpha_n|$. Then R becomes a Banach algebra. It is clear that R is generated by polynomials in the function h where $h(\zeta) = \zeta$: $\mathrm{R} = \mathrm{R}(h)$. To determine the maximal ideal space of $\mathrm{R}(h)$ it suffices to determine $\sigma(h)$. Clearly, $\sigma(h)$ contains the disc $|\lambda| \leq 1$ since the function f with $f(\zeta) = \lambda - \zeta$ cannot have an inverse function with absolutely convergent power series when $|\lambda| \leq 1$. Furthermore, if $|\lambda| > 1$, then $(\lambda - \zeta)^{-1} = \sum_{n=0}^{\infty} \lambda^{-n-1}\zeta^n$ which converges absolutely. Thus $\sigma(h)$ is precisely the unit disc

[5] Due to the author.

$|\lambda| \leq 1$. We have seen earlier that for an algebra $R(h)$, $\mathfrak{M} = \sigma(h)$. Finally, if $f \in R(h)$, f^{-1} fails to exist if and only if f belongs to some maximal ideal. We have therefore proved that the reciprocal of an absolutely convergent series f is also absolutely convergent if and only if $f(\zeta) \neq 0$, $|\zeta| \leq 1$.

A mild elaboration of the above argument proves a similar type of result (due to Wiener) on the ring R of absolutely convergent Fourier series $f(x) = \sum_{n=-\infty}^{\infty} \alpha_n \exp(inx)$ with $\|f\| = \sum_{n=-\infty}^{\infty} |\alpha_n|$. Here R has two generators: $h_1(x) = \exp(ix)$, $h_2(x) = \exp(-ix)$. Clearly $\mathfrak{M}$ contains the loop $[0, 2\pi]$ with $0 = 2\pi$. An easy argument shows that $\mathfrak{M} = [0, 2\pi]$. Hence the reciprocal of an absolutely convergent Fourier series is absolutely convergent if and only if it does not vanish. Note that R has no radical and that in the representation of R into $C_{\mathfrak{M}}$ the image of R is dense in $C_{\mathfrak{M}}$ (in the metric of $C_{\mathfrak{M}}$) and is not identical with $C_{\mathfrak{M}}$.

SELECTED REFERENCES

Banach, S., *Théorie des opérations linéaires*, Warsaw, 1932, Hafner Publishing Co., New York.

Berberian, S. K., *Introduction to Hilbert Space*, Oxford University Press, New York, 1961.

Bourbaki, N., *Espaces vectoriels topologiques*, Hermann & Cie., Paris, 1955.

Day, M. M., *Normed Linear Spaces*, Ergebnisse der Mathematik, Berlin, 1958.

Dunford, N., and Schwartz, J., *Linear Operators*, Part I, Interscience, New York, 1958.

Halmos, P., *Introduction to Hilbert Space*, Chelsea, New York, 1951.

Hille, E., and Phillips, R., *Functional Analysis and Semi-Groups*, Amer. Math. Soc. Coll. Publ. 31, Providence, 1957.

Loomis, L., *An Introduction to Abstract Harmonic Analysis*, van Nostrand Co., Princeton, 1953.

Naimark, M., *Normed Rings*, P. Noordhoff N. V., Groningen, 1959.

Rickart, C., *Banach Algebras*, Van Nostrand Co., Princeton, 1960.

Riesz, F. and Sz. Nagy, B., *Leçons d'analyse fonctionelle*, Akadémiai Kiadó, Budapest, 1953.

Stone, M., *Linear Transformations in Hilbert Space*, Amer. Math. Soc. Coll. Publ. 15, Providence, 1932.

INDEX